DISCOVERING
THE WEATHER

*Cover picture: moisture particles lit up by the sun,
form a luminous veil above billowing cumulus cloud.*

*Opposite: multiple streaks of lightning illuminate the
mountain shores of Lake Lugano, Italy, during a
violent thunderstorm.*

DISCOVERING
THE WEATHER

Published by

STONEHENGE

in association with

The American Museum of Natural History

The contributor
Peter Wright graduated from London University in 1964.
Following six years with the British Meteorological Office, where
he worked in the long-range forecasting branch, he held the post
of Senior Research Associate at the University of East Anglia. He
has spent several years at the University of Hawaii investigating
the interaction between oceans and climate, and has written
articles for many scientific journals. Peter Wright is now a
professional meteorological consultant and writer.

The consultant
Harold M. Gibson began making weather forecasts while in the
US Air Force and later studied at St Louis University, from which he
graduated in 1955. After joining the National Weather Service he
was employed in all areas of the United States, gaining special
experience of tornadoes, and aviation, marine and public
forecasting. He is now in charge of the National Weather Service
Forecast Office in New York City, a post he has held since 1971.

The American Museum of Natural History
Stonehenge Press wishes to extend particular thanks to
Dr. Thomas D. Nicholson, Director of the Museum, and Mr. David
D. Ryus, Vice President, for their counsel and assistance in
creating this volume.

Stonehenge Press Inc.:
Publisher: John Canova
Editor: Ezra Bowen
Deputy Editor: Carolyn Tasker

Trewin Copplestone Books Ltd.:
Editorial Director: James Clark
Managing Editor: Barbara Horn
Executive Editor: Penny Clarke

Created, designed and produced by
Trewin Copplestone Books Ltd, London.

Library of Congress Card Number: 81-52418
Printed in U.S.A. by Rand McNally & Co.
First printing
ISBN 0-86706-008-5
ISBN 0-86706-059-X (lib. bdg.)
ISBN 0-86706-028-X (retail ed.)

Set in Monophoto Rockwell Light by
SX Composing Ltd, Rayleigh, Essex, England
Separation by Gilchrist Bros. Ltd., Leeds, England
Printed in U.S.A. by Rand McNally & Co.

Contents

The World of Weather

Everyone on earth lives with an endlessly evolving, ever fascinating force called the weather. But very few people have any understanding of the weather, or, indeed, can even say what the weather really is.

Weather can be defined as the condition of the air at a particular place and time – a spring snowstorm in Paris on Thursday, rain in Caracas in July, an early fall hurricane roaring off the coast of Cuba, a sunny sky above Melbourne, Australia at Christmas. The weather is around us at this moment, on this day, throughout this month, taking place in the atmosphere – the envelope of gases that surrounds the earth. Of one thing we can be certain: the weather will change – in some areas frequently, occasionally violently, and often quite fast. A bright, warm October can turn to a dank November overnight; Thursday's drizzle becomes Friday's clear morning; and within the space of a few minutes an apparently perfect summer noon can explode into a stormy afternoon.

The sum total of all such weather in a region over an extended period of time is called the climate. And while the daily weather within this extended time may be very different, overall the climate in an area takes on a broadly stable set of characteristics. For example, the winter climate is said to be generally cool and damp – although a particular winter day in London may be pleasantly mild and dry. Any real changes in climate are relatively slow and measured in decades, centuries, and ages. Perhaps the best example is the last so-called Ice Age, actually a glacial period. Then, enormous sheets of moving ice stretched down from the Arctic to touch the present sites of St. Louis, Missouri and Cracow, Poland, transforming their climates to something similar to that of southern Greenland today.

Humans have carefully watched this shifting display of climate and weather since well before the beginning of history, for the weather, then as now, influenced every human activity. In ancient civilizations man built elaborate astronomical observatories to look at the sun and moon – and thereby, perhaps learn something about the seasons. The Greeks, as early as the fifth century BC, posted daily weather observations for the use of mariners. Accurate prediction of the weather, the dream of every human society, developed first as a folk art, based on everything from the configuration of spider webs to the color of a sunset.

However, the scientific study of the weather, called meteorology, from the Greek word *meteoron* meaning "phenomenon in the sky," did not make its first real advances until the seventeenth century with the development of the thermometer to measure air temperature and the barometer to measure atmospheric pressure. With these instruments – and others that followed – those who study the science of weather, known as meteorologists, could begin to diagnose the physical condition of the atmosphere much as a doctor diagnoses a patient. This is because temperature and pressure, along with the water content of the atmosphere and wind (the name given by meteorologists to any moving mass of air) are the ingredients of the weather.

Today meteorologists probe and sample the atmosphere with sophisticated instruments which are often carried aloft by rockets or balloons. They watch the weather of a particular region by studying information provided by satellites orbiting high above the earth, and try to make sense of their observations with the help of giant computers.

Meteorologists engage in all of this research in the hope of correctly predicting – or forecasting – tomorrow's weather. In addition, as this book will show, they are beginning to understand some of the complex natural forces that govern every sort of weather people are likely to experience.

They have succeeded to an impressive degree: consider only the saving in life and property made possible by hurricane tracking and early flood warning bulletins. Nevertheless, because of the incredible complexity of the weather, meteorology remains an inexact and continually evolving science.

The Global Circulation

Weather is the result of complex interactions between the sun, the earth and the atmosphere. The sun and the earth are of prime importance for it is their size, heat and general behavior that cause the series of atmospheric events we call weather.

Together the sun and earth form the major components in an enormous heat-exchange system that circulates warm air toward the Poles, while moving cold polar air toward the Equator. The reason for this unending exchange of warm air for cool is a natural law called the second law of thermodynamics, which, simply stated, says that heat always passes in one direction – from warmer areas to cooler ones.

Because of the position of the earth's axis relative to the sun, solar rays shine more directly upon the Equator than on the Poles, thus making the earth and its blanket of air at the Equator comparatively warmer. Following the second law, the Equator's warm air always moves toward the colder polar regions. Moreover, since warm air is also comparatively light, the equatorial air rises above the earth as it moves north or south, thus creating a kind of vacuum that is constantly being filled by cold heavy air moving from the Poles.

If the earth were standing still, and were made of a single piece of solid material, all the movements of air – which we call wind – would be in two directions. The warm, high-level equatorial air would move directly north, while the cold polar air would move directly south. But the spinning of the earth affects these winds so that the major global circulation systems flow toward the east or west rather than directly north or south. This bending effect on the winds is called the Coriolis effect, after the nineteenth century mathematician Gaspard de Coriolis, the first to explain it. The Coriolis effect gives a constant westward swing to winds in the tropic zone.

This varied circulation system helps explain the climate near the Equator. This region is frequently cloudy and wet because the warm, moist rising air produces clouds and rain. The east coasts of continents and islands in this area are wet because there the winds blow off the ocean. Since sailing ships

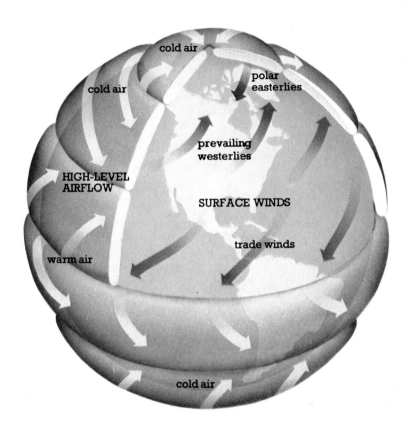

This cutaway diagram of the earth's surface winds (blue arrows) and high-level air circulation (white arrows) shows the broad patterns produced by the combination of the sun's heat and the earth's rotation. The white arrows at the equatorial latitudes indicate warm air that rises and moves north or south away from the Equator; the white arrows near the Arctic indicate warm air moving northward, where it cools and sinks. White arrows in the middle latitudes show polar air moving toward the Equator. Closer to the surface the major winds are divided into three belts: the trade winds of tropical latitudes (once used by sailing ships) blowing toward the Equator, the prevailing westerlies in the middle latitudes, and the polar easterlies. Note that wind directions at all levels form sweeping curves. This is because the earth's rotation bends winds to the right in the northern hemisphere and to the left in the southern hemisphere.

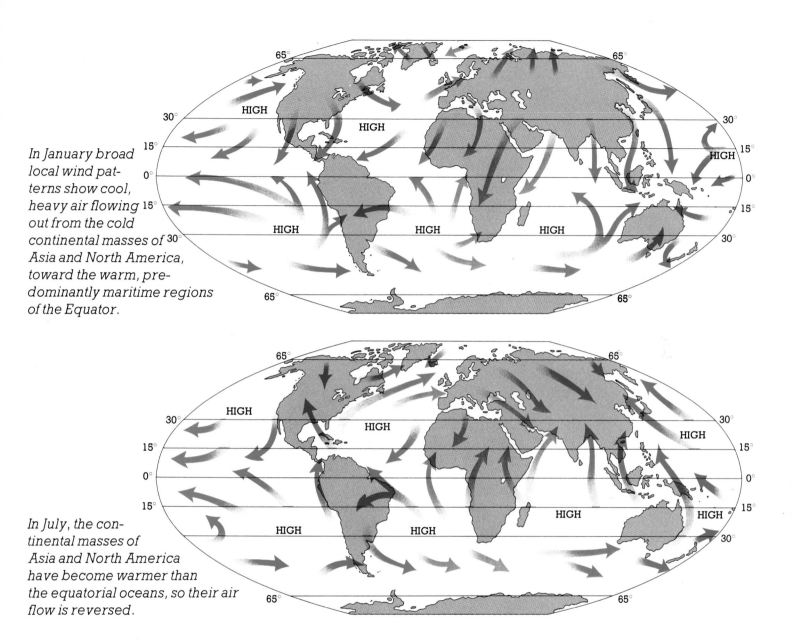

In January broad local wind patterns show cool, heavy air flowing out from the cold continental masses of Asia and North America, toward the warm, predominantly maritime regions of the Equator.

In July, the continental masses of Asia and North America have become warmer than the equatorial oceans, so their air flow is reversed.

trading between continents could take advantage of these ocean winds, they became known as trade winds.

At the polar regions the cold air begins to sink and spread out. Because of the Coriolis effect, this sinking air does not move directly south, but like the trade winds near the Equator, takes a westward swing. However, since meteorologists name winds according to the direction from which they come, the westward moving polar winds are known as the polar easterlies.

In the middle latitudes, the global circulation is more complicated. This region – between 30 and 65 degrees north and south of the Equator – is called the temperate zone. It is known to meteorologists as a transition area where the weather is, on the average, very changeable. In the northern hemisphere, for example, the high-level winds coming in from the northwest are cold, while the winds closer to the surface are from the southwest and typically warm. In this transition area warm and cold air have a continual battle. The lighter air rises and pushes towards the Poles, while cold air surges towards the Equator.

The Atmosphere

The atmosphere, which surrounds and sustains life, is the stage setting within which the drama of weather is played. Extending from the earth's surface to perhaps 600 miles or more into space, the atmosphere divides into several layers, each comprised of gases in varying quantities and densities. The predominant gases in the lowest layer, the troposphere, are oxygen, nitrogen, traces (about 0.03 per cent) of carbon dioxide and – most important for the weather – water vapor.

Virtually all of the weather as we know it – with constant changes from wet to dry, clear to cloudy, hot to cold, windy to still – and vice versa – takes place in the troposphere. This is mainly because all but the tiniest traces of water vapor – the stuff of which fog, clouds, rain and all other forms of precipitation is made – occur in the troposphere. Without this water vapor there would be no life.

The troposphere varies in thickness, from about five miles over the Poles to about 10 miles over the Equator. Where the water vapor begins to disappear and no clouds form, the troposphere ends and the stratosphere begins. This atmospheric layer contains almost no clouds and, hence, virtually no weather. Here too, oxygen and most of the other life-sustaining gases thin out.

As the altitude changes, so too does the temperature. For example, the average temperature about 10 miles above the Equator has fallen to nearly –50°F. This happens because the earth and the water vapor in the troposphere act as radiators, absorbing and giving off the sun's heat.

Beyond the troposphere, neither the earth's heat nor water vapor is a factor in determining atmospheric temperature. In the stratosphere the temperature becomes warmer with increased altitude because of the dominance of solar radiation. Then in the next layer, the mesophere, the temperature turns cold again, in part because of the reaction of a gas called ozone that blocks out the sun's ultraviolet rays. The temperature continues to drop until it reaches 120°F or more below zero. Then, at perhaps 50 miles over the earth, where the thermosphere begins, the

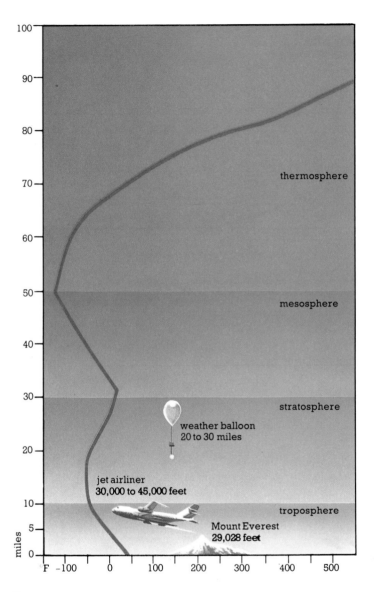

This diagram shows, in simplified form, the principal layers of the earth's atmosphere, and the general way in which temperature (red line) varies with altitude. The highest point on earth is Mt. Everest (29,028 feet) extending just beyond the middle of the troposphere. The thin air at the top of the troposphere, 10 miles above the earth, is the upper limit for most commercial aircraft. A light weather balloon, however could go higher, and may soar up to about 30 miles.

gases – under the direct influence of the sun – become so thinly concentrated that they all but disappear.

Although these upper layers contain no weather in the popular use of the term, they affect events in the troposphere by shielding the earth from the searing rays of the sun. In addition these upper layers together contribute about 25 per cent of the atmospheric weight that presses down upon the earth's surface.

The troposphere contributes the other 75 per cent of the atmosphere's weight, through the presence of the relatively dense gases – including water vapor. Vapor enters the atmosphere by evaporation from oceans, seas, and lakes, and to a lesser extent from wet ground and vegetation. Heat is needed for evaporation to occur, and this heat is taken from the surface, which therefore becomes cooler.

This heat is not lost, but is stored in the vapor as hidden, or latent, heat. The vapor is carried by winds to higher levels of the atmosphere and to different parts of the world. As a result, water vapor may be

Sea fog, seen here cloaking a ship in Hamburg harbor, Germany, is one of the most menacing forms of condensation. It occurs whenever moist air is significantly warmer than the surface over which it passes.

found throughout the troposphere and over all regions, oceans and continents. Eventually, water vapor condenses into liquid water or solid ice and falls to the ground as precipitation – rain, snow or hail. In condensing, it releases its latent heat to the atmosphere. Thus if water evaporates into the air from a tropical ocean and winds then carry it to a temperate continent, where it condenses and falls as rain, this provides a very effective means of carrying not only water but also heat from places that have plenty to places that are short of both.

9

The Air Around Us

In the air around us, the temperature, pressure and moisture content are affected by the fourth critical ingredient that makes up our weather: the wind. As we know, wind is the popular name for a moving mass of air. Nearly everyone is familiar with winds that blow from north, south, east or west – that is across the earth's surface, or horizontally. But winds also blow vertically – as bird-watchers know from seeing gulls or crows sail upward on rising currents of warm air, or from watching a hawk sink down rapidly on a descending cold current.

Most vertical air currents are much gentler than horizontal winds. But they are vitally important, because they can generate many different types of weather. When air rises it expands, because the pressure on it becomes less. As it rises, the air cools. Because it cools, its moisture content increases. Eventually the rising air may reach a level at which it becomes saturated with moisture. If it rises still farther, vapor starts condensing to form clouds. Nearly all clouds and rain originate in upcurrents of air.

The line of clouds hanging above these mountain peaks in eastern Switzerland has resulted from the cooling of warm, vapor-laden air that has risen above the sloping terrain.

As winds (white arrows) blow across an expanse of ocean they pick up moisture, in the form of water vapor, by evaporation (red arrows). This vapor may be carried hundreds of miles inland until the winds rise to cross a high coastline or mountain range. Condensation then takes place until clouds form, and the moisture falls to the ground as rain.

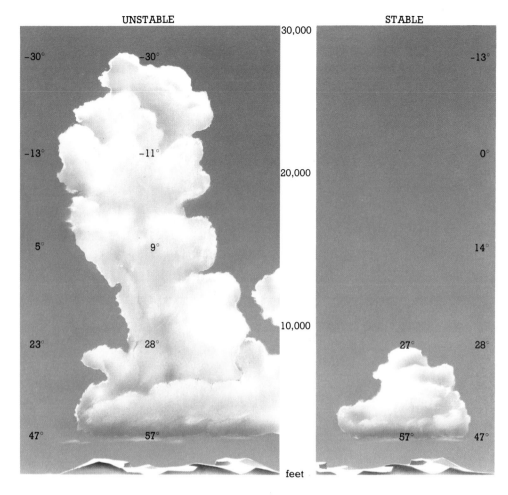

UNSTABLE

-30° -30°

-13° -11°

5° 9°

23° 28°

47° 57°

30,000

20,000

10,000

feet

STABLE

-13°

0°

14°

27° 28°

57° 47°

This diagram shows the visible difference between unstable and stable air. If the overall temperature above a region decreases severely with height (far left), then any warm segments or bubbles of air – rising through colder surrounding air – will remain relatively warmer and continue to rise. As the bubbles rise, their moisture condenses to form a tall cloud or clouds. However, if the surrounding air cools only moderately with increased height (near left), air bubbles soon stop rising and only small clouds form. Numbers on the clouds indicate the temperature of the air within.

One reason why air starts to rise is because of temperature differences from place to place. Such differences are most marked on sunny days over land, when the air above some surfaces, such as asphalt or bare soil, becomes warmer than that over adjacent surfaces, such as trees or lakes. The warmer masses of air, which meteorologists call bubbles, then start to rise. The air between the rising bubbles sinks to compensate. This type of air movement is called convection.

Once a bubble of air has started to rise, it will continue to do so as long as it remains warmer than its surroundings. As it rises, it cools, initially at a rate of 5.4°F per 1000 feet. But its surroundings also cool with height. Eventually the bubble will reach its condensation level and clouds will start to form. The condensation in such clouds releases latent heat, making the rising air even warmer than it would have been. This increases the difference in tempera-ture between the rising air and the surrounding air. The atmosphere is then said to be unstable. As long as the atmosphere remains unstable, the bubble will grow bigger and rise farther, producing a tall cloud. This cloud may become so saturated with moisture that rain or snow begins to fall from it.

On the other hand, if the rate of decrease of the temperature in the air surrounding the bubble is quite small, or if the temperature actually rises with height – as it sometimes does – then the rising air bubble will soon become colder than its surround-ings. The bubble will then stop rising. In this situation the atmosphere is said to be stable. Bubbles may never reach their condensation level, in which case no clouds will form – or the bubble will produce only small, shallow clouds. When clouds do form, con-densation may stop before the air becomes so saturated that precipitation begins. This is typically the case in stable air.

Oceans, Currents and Climate

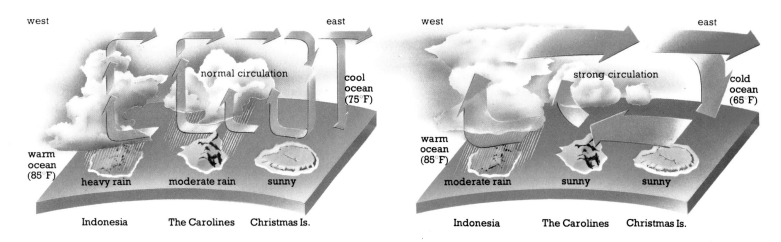

The oceans are the features on earth that have the greatest influence on the long-term climates of the world's regions. They also strongly influence the daily weather. The most obvious contribution the oceans make is their moisture. Every day millions upon millions of tons of water vapor rise from the oceans to replenish the moisture that is continually falling as precipitation all over the world.

The other great influence of the oceans comes in the transfer of heat between the oceans and the atmosphere. The most subtle influence is by the transfer of latent heat. As moisture evaporates into the air, it carries along the heat used to evaporate it. When such warm, vapor-laden air continues to rise, the heat remains with the vapor until the air reaches an altitude where cooler temperatures condense the moisture into clouds and perhaps precipitation. However, when the moisture begins to condense, it releases its latent heat back into the air, slowing the rate of condensation and allowing the remaining portions of moist air to continue rising. The moisture gradually condenses into an even larger, taller cloud, until the temperature at the top of the cloud is the same as that of the surrounding air.

By far the more important influence of ocean heat, however, is upon the world's winds – and through

This pair of stylized diagrams indicates typical weather (left) over Christmas Island, in the mid-Pacific, and over the Caroline Islands and Indonesia, in the western Pacific, during periods of normal ocean temperatures. If the eastern Pacific cools significantly, the weather pattern changes, as shown above.

them, upon the ocean currents that so profoundly affect the earth's range of climates. The oceans' water holds heat longer (and remains cool longer) during a period of changing temperature than does a more solid substance, such as a continental land mass. Around the world, water temperatures vary – cold at the Poles, warm at the Equator, to take the two most familiar and extreme examples. The temperature variations in the water cause the air lying above the oceans to move, from warmer to cooler. In other words, they make the winds blow. And when the air moves, it carries temperature changes with it, thus affecting the weather wherever it goes.

When the wind blows strongly and steadily across a great expanse of ocean for a long time, friction from the moving air begins to drag the water along with it. Once the water has been set in motion, its momentum, aided by the wind, keeps it moving in a steady flow we call a current. This interaction between wind and water, and water and wind, has created the great global currents. These include the Gulf Stream, which brings tropical Caribbean water to the high latitudes of western Europe and creates a comparatively warm climate in Britain, which otherwise would be as cold as Labrador. Because of both the Coriolis effect, which bends winds because of the earth's rotation, and the fact that all ocean currents sooner or later strike land barriers that turn the water from its course, the currents – like the winds that cause them – tend to move in circular paths. North of the Equator the currents generally rotate clockwise; to the south they rotate counterclockwise.

Occasionally, a temporary but powerful alteration in the prevailing wind patterns will change the temperature of some portion of the upper ocean. When this occurs the air temperature above that region also changes and this may affect the weather thousands of miles away. For example, the normal temperature in the western Pacific is about 85°F while that in the eastern Pacific fluctuates around 75°F. Under these conditions, the trade winds bring sunny weather to the islands in mid-ocean, with increasingly heavy rains to the west. But when a strong, cold wind blows out to sea from South America's Andes mountains, the offshore water may drop 10°F or more, setting up a horizontal temperature difference that sends new, more powerful winds across the Pacific. This causes a drought in mid-ocean, and sunny weather to the west, with rain continuing to fall only on distant Indonesia.

The arrows on the map below indicate the locations and directions of the major ocean currents set in motion by the global wind systems. By carrying warm water to cool latitudes, and cool water to warm latitudes, these currents have a major effect on the world's climates.

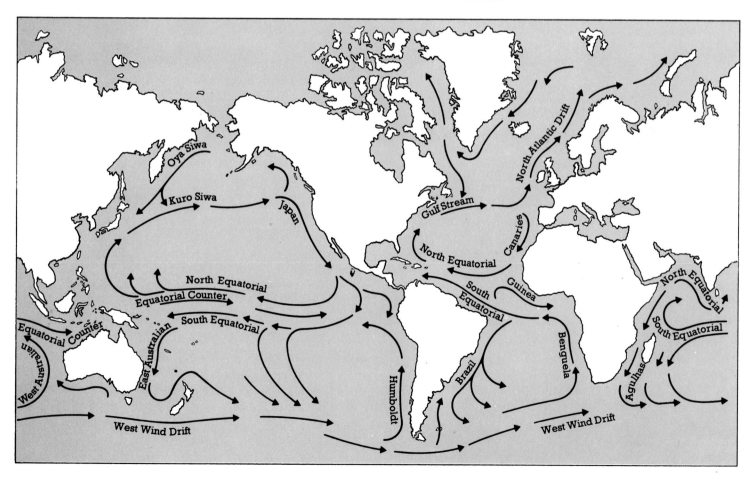

Pressure Systems

The variations in atmospheric pressure that exist in the air around us tend to arrange themselves into four basic patterns, known as pressure systems. Each of these pressure systems carries with it certain characteristic types of weather. At the same time, the weather within the systems and at their fringes, where they adjoin other systems, changes as these shifting patterns of pressure move across the face of the earth. The four systems are known as lows, troughs, highs and ridges.

A low is an area where the atmospheric pressure is less than that of the surrounding areas. In depicting atmospheric pressure on a weather map, meteorologists draw lines, called isobars, connecting points of equal pressure. As a result, a low pressure system on a weather map resembles a series of concentric circles with the circle at the center representing the area of lowest pressure. The size of a low is frequently enormous – a typical low may cover the entire eastern half of Canada.

A low can be thought of as rather like a vast bowl, with the highest pressures at the edges of the system corresponding to the rim of the bowl, and the center of the low-pressure system corresponding to the bottom. Just as water tends to run down the inside of a bowl toward the lowest point, air tends to flow toward the center of the low, along what is called the gradient of pressure. The greater the difference in pressure between inner and outer parts of the low, the steeper the gradient of pressure, and the stronger the air flow. Thus, extreme lows tend to become regions of powerful winds.

However, the air does not move in a straight line to the center of a low pressure system because, like most weather phenomena, pressure systems are affected by the earth's rotation. Air sliding down toward the center of a low gets diverted into a spiral, flowing counterclockwise in the northern hemisphere, and clockwise in the southern. Meteorologists call low pressure systems cyclones – which can be confusing to laymen, who sometimes apply the same word to the violent wind phenomena that are properly called tornadoes or hurricanes.

When the air reaches the center of a low, it tends to rise. When it rises, it cools, and its moisture condenses into rain or snow. Thus, lows tend to bring cloudy, wet weather, as well as winds. In the temperate zones a low usually moves from west to east, blown along by the prevailing westerlies. It usually brings warm air with clouds and rain, and when it has passed, the temperature tends to drop.

A trough is an elongated extension of a low. The area in front of an eastward-moving trough gets showers or thunderstorms, while the area to the west of the trough tends to get cooler weather with clearing skies.

A high is an area where the atmospheric pressure is higher than in surrounding areas. Like a low, a high pressure system appears on a weather map as a series of concentric circles, but with the highest pressure at the center. And virtually everything else about a high is opposite to a low. Highs typically bring clear, sunny weather. Winds blow out from the center of a high, though not as strongly as winds move into the center of an intense low. The winds around a high in the northern hemisphere swirl clockwise – and in the opposite direction south of the Equator. A ridge is an extension of a high, the opposite of a trough. And to complete the opposites, meteorologists call high pressure systems anticyclones.

The simplified weather map on the right, constructed from measurements taken at 7 a.m. Eastern Standard Time on January 12, 1975, shows the two main types of pressure systems. Arrows indicate wind direction; numbers show the atmospheric pressure in units called millibars (1013.2 millibars is normal pressure at sea level). The curving lines that surround the high and low centers are called isobars – lines that connect points of equal barometric pressure. The photographs at top show typical weather around a high (left) and in the vicinity of a low (right) at the two locations indicated on the map.

Monument Valley

Quebec City

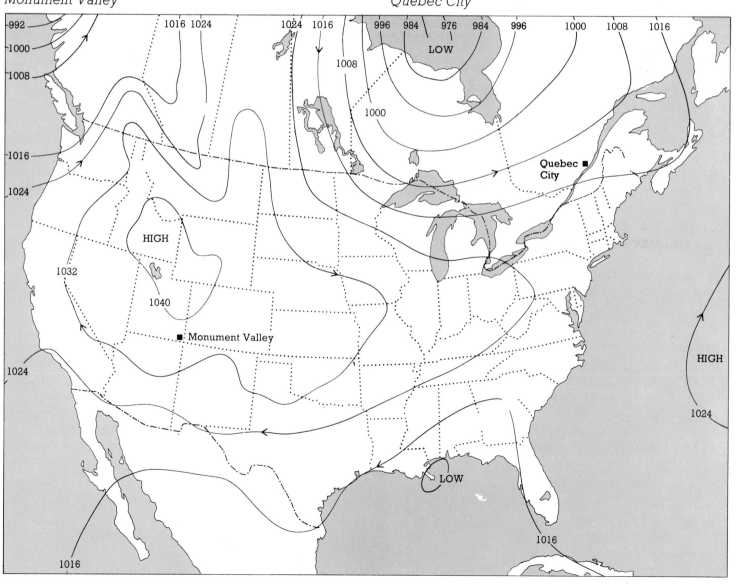

Air Masses and Fronts

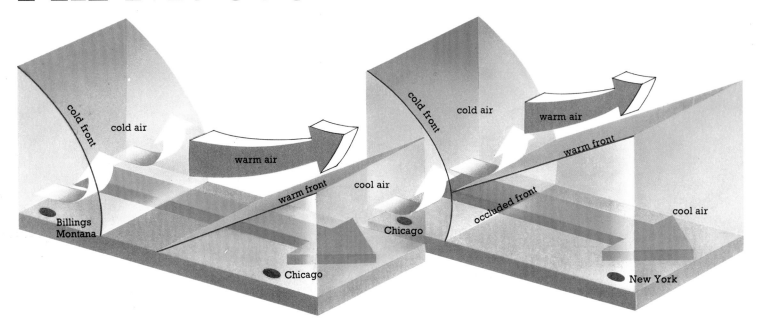

If air remains stationary for long enough, it takes on some of the characteristics of the earth's surface lying beneath it. Air above the Caribbean, for example, would become warm and moist, while air over northern Canada would become cold and dry. As a result, meteorologists classify the four main kinds of air masses according to their places of origin: air masses called polar continental form over very cold lands such as northern Canada; those called polar maritime form over cold northern seas such as the Arctic Ocean; tropic continental air masses are born over warm inland regions such as the Sahara; and tropic maritime air masses originate over oceans near the Equator.

Once a mass of air has acquired its individual character of temperature and moisture, it tends to retain that character and not to mix with other air masses, even after it moves from its place of origin. Thus, there is a more or less definite boundary between different air masses. Meteorologists have named these boundaries fronts, because they can be regarded as the front lines of a battle for dominance in the atmosphere, in which each air mass tries to displace the other.

We know that the most frequent and extreme changes in weather occur in the temperate zones,

Cold, warm and occluded fronts are illustrated in the pair of diagrams above. Cold air from the west converges upon a mass of warm air, pushing it forward and upward (left). The warm air encroaches on cool air to the east, creating a warm front. The cold air continues to overtake the warm air, separating it from the ground. Finally, the cold air moves forward to meet the cool air east of the warm front, forming an occluded front (right).

roughly between latitudes 30 degrees and 65 degrees. It is here that the masses of polar and tropical air most often meet, or converge, along an undulating line known as a polar front. Frequently one of the undulations on the polar front grows larger, and an area of low pressure develops on the front at this point. This phenomenon is called a wave, and it travels eastwards along the polar front. The forward arc of the wave is called a warm front, because there the warm tropical air, flowing counterclockwise around the low, displaces the polar air in its path. The following arc of the wave is called a cold front, because along that arc the polar air displaces the warm air ahead.

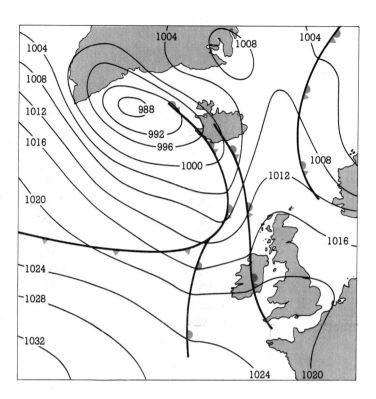

In this satellite picture taken in 1979, the whirl of dense clouds shows a storm brought on by a low centered in the North Atlantic west of Iceland. Note that the predominant curve of the clouds is counterclockwise, reflecting the typical pattern of winds around a low in the northern hemisphere. Note, too, that as the winds move toward the heart of the low at upper left, the spiral pattern becomes tighter and a dense circle of clouds covers the low's stormy center.

A map (above) of the low illustrated at left shows the center to have a pressure of only 988 millibars, indicating a severe storm. The heavy lines indicate the system's fronts, with each front mirrored by a curved line of clouds in the photograph. Triangles (here in blue) are the weatherman's indicator of a cold front; semicircles (red) indicate warm fronts, and semicircles and triangles on the same side of the line (purple) stand for occluded fronts.

Most of the lows formed on a polar front deepen; that is, the pressure in the center of the low (around the crest of the wave) keeps falling, the low grows larger, and the contending air masses are drawn deeper into ther counterclockwise spiral (clockwise in the southern hemisphere) around the system.

Since warm air is lighter than cold air, the tropic air behind the warm front tends to rise over the polar air as the warm front advances. Similarly, the polar air behind the following cold front tends to roll under tropic air ahead. As the fronts continue to move around the low, more and more of the warm air is lifted off the ground, and the sector of warm air between the two fronts narrows. Since cold air tends

to move faster than warm air, the cold front eventually pushes under the last of the warm air and catches up the warm front. The warm air is now said to be occluded, that is, completely separated, from the surface of the earth. Therefore, the front formed when the cold front overtakes the warm front is called an occluded front.

In the occluded front, the displaced warm air rises more slowly, while cold air continues to flow into the low near the ground. The low begins to fill, or weaken. By this time, however, a new low may have formed to the west, and may completely absorb the old one.

Weather on the Move

Although pressure systems, air masses, and the fronts where they clash, are invisible to the naked eye, they result in the fascinating and endless weather display that sweeps across the sky.

The following description is of a typical sequence of weather that might occur in the northern temperate zone as a wave passes eastward over a given area. For analogous conditions in the southern hemisphere, simply substitute "south" for "north."

The first sign of the approach of the warm front – the leading arc of the wave – will be the appearance of thin wisps of clouds high in the sky. When the front has moved closer, these clouds increase and thicken until the sky becomes covered by a thin, milky layer. The barometer shows falling pressure, and the wind blows increasingly hard from the southeast. The clouds gradually thicken and lower until they completely hide the sun or moon. Then it starts to rain. The rain will be light at first, but it gradually becomes heavier and continues for a few hours. The clouds then lower still further, and may cover the tops of hills. The wind changes to southwesterly, the pressure stops falling, the rain eases off, and the skies slowly clear. The air feels muggy and warmer. These are all signs that the warm front itself has passed and that the warm sector of the wave has arrived.

After a few hours, or perhaps even a day or two, it becomes darker as thick clouds arrive. Soon, heavy rain starts to fall, and may last from a few minutes to two hours. This is the sign that the following cold front has arrived. Some cold fronts may produce a line of thunderstorms, called a squall line, which can be as long as 500 miles. But this is the climax of the storm. After the front has passed the change in the weather is sometimes almost miraculous. The heavy

This diagram below shows the weather that typically occurs in the temperate zone when a warm front, trailed by a cold front (left), overtakes a mass of cool air (right). Note that the characteristically slow-moving warm air mass, traveling from west to east, gradually rides up the slope of denser, cooler air ahead, slowly creating a wide band of rain clouds that deposits rain over an area that may be 200–300 miles across. The faster-moving trailing cold front, its leading edge blunted by contact with the warm air mass, quickly forces moisture to high altitudes, where it condenses in a tall thunder cloud.

DIRECTION OF WEATHER MOVEMENT

warm sector

warm front

cold front

cold sector

heavy showers

steady rain

cold sector

rain stops, the barometer indicates that pressure is rising, and the clouds move away toward the southeast as fresh clear air blows in from the west or northwest. The sun or stars come out, the humidity is low, and the weather feels very refreshing.

Although the cool dry air is a welcome change after the muggy air of the warm sector and the rain of the cold front, new clouds may quickly form and bring showers, especially in regions where the wind is blowing off large bodies of water, such as the British Isles and the southeast side of the Great Lakes. In winter the cold may soon get too cold for comfort and give off heavy showers of snow. However, after a day or two the showers usually die away, the winds drop and the air gets a little warmer. The wave has completely gone. The region is in a ridge of high pressure, and people can enjoy the dry, sunny weather. Then cirrus clouds begin to appear in the west and gradually spread across the sky all over again as the next wave approaches.

Of course, no wave brings exactly the same sort of weather. The cold front may be weak and give no rain, or the warm sector may be sunny instead of cloudy. But the general sequence is common, and if you remember it you will often be able to make a correct weather forecast.

The gauzy shreds of high-altitude clouds in the picture below herald an approaching low.

Jet Streams

The wind patterns of the upper atmosphere – at a height of three to six miles – are not subject to friction from the land surface and are therefore much more regular than the low-level winds. A large area of low pressure lies over each Pole and a band of higher pressure surrounds the tropics. Between these two zones winds blow roughly from west to east in a series of giant waves which are alternately troughs of low pressure and ridges of high pressure. At these upper levels, low pressure always contains cold air, so in the latitudes where the waves occur the temperature varies from cold in the troughs to warm in the ridges.

Wind charts show two irregular bands of closely

The winds of the jet stream form a series of constantly shifting waves around the Poles, carrying weather systems from west to east. The spiral of clouds in this illustration represents a low; as a result the jet stream makes a small ripple above it.

spaced isobars stretching around each hemisphere. These indicate very strong winds – called jet streams – which often reach speeds as great as 180 miles per hour and form a sharp boundary between cold and warm air. The jet streams are not fixed but writhe about like snakes as the waves change their position from day to day. Upper-air charts show big waves that remain almost stationary, and smaller ripples that move through the big waves from west to east. Underneath each ripple in the upper atmosphere there is a low-pressure area closer to the earth.

The winds in the upper atmosphere control the movement of lows and highs in the lower atmosphere, so that a low situated under a strong eastward-moving jet stream will move rapidly along in the same direction. Skilled meteorologists can recognize patterns in the upper winds that can cause new lows and highs to form in the lower atmosphere. Therefore an upper-air chart that shows these winds is extremely useful for making a weather forecast.

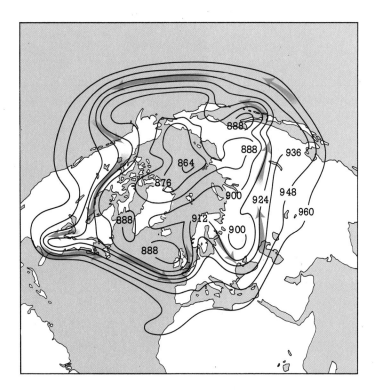

This upper-atmosphere polar chart of the earth's northern hemisphere on September 18, 1981, shows the jet stream (arrows) as a twisting band of winds, interrupted by cold pools of low-pressure air. The numbers give pressure in millibars.

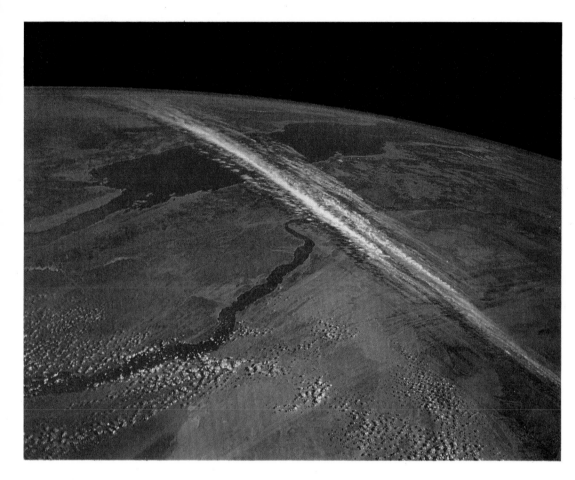

This dramatic photograph, taken from Gemini 12, shows a band of cirrus clouds lying along the subtropical jet stream above the Red Sea and Nile valley.

Although the upper-air flow influences the movement of the lower air, the reverse is also true. In other words, the upper and lower layers interact. If a low-pressure area near the earth's surface grows wide, it twists the jet stream and makes one of the waves bigger. Sometimes the jet stream gets twisted so much that a wave breaks off and drifts toward the Equator. The ends of the broken jet stream then connect up again behind it. The breakaway, which consists of a large mass of cold air cut off from the main supply, is called a cold pool. Since it has broken out of the main stream, there is nothing to move it along, and it remains stationary. A cold pool can bring a week of cold showery weather to places that normally enjoy warm sunshine.

Sometimes the flow pattern gets mixed up. A big cold pool of low-pressure air gets stuck in low latitudes, and a big warm pool of high-pressure air gets stuck in high latitudes. This pattern is called a block – because it blocks the usual movement of weather systems from west to east. A block can surprise people living near the Arctic Circle with a spell of fine, warm weather, while people in Spain may get a spell of cold, showery weather in the summer. Blocks sometimes persist for a week or more and are the cause of some heatwaves and spells of bitter winter weather.

The jet stream in the southern hemisphere is always powerful because the greater area of ice around the South Pole creates a sharper difference in temperature – and consequently in pressure – between the polar regions and the tropics. Blocks and cold pools are infrequent but they sometimes occur over eastern Australia and the Tasman Sea for a week or two. In the northern hemisphere the jet stream is strongest in winter, when the temperature contrast between polar and equatorial regions is most marked. The continents, with their high mountain ranges, tend to disrupt the winds, and as a result blocks are more common than in the southern hemisphere.

Climates

No two places on earth have exactly the same type of weather. New York City has a hot, humid summer and a cold, snowy winter, while Rome is hot and dry in summer but mostly mild in winter. Some places get plenty of sunshine and little rainfall, others have alternating spells of warm and cold weather. Different places get different mixtures, so we say that they have different climates. Weather is the daily meteorological event – sunshine, rain, snow and so on. Climate can be defined as the average mixture of weather that a place experiences, usually over a period of years, or even centuries.

People have been measuring the weather in different parts of the world for many years. If we look at records of average temperatures and rainfall for several places, we can compare their climates.

	Temperature (Fahrenheit)	Inches of rainfall	Hours of sunshine
Stockholm	43	22.4	1973
London	51	22.9	1533
Toronto	45	32.2	2026
Los Angeles	62	13	3200
Melbourne	58	25.7	2044

From the yearly averages in the table we can see that Los Angeles has a much warmer climate than Toronto, with less rain and more sunshine. London's climate is warmer than that of Stockholm but has a little more rain and less sunshine. Both Toronto and Melbourne are wetter and sunnier than London, but Toronto is colder and Melbourne warmer.

Meteorologists have worked out these averages for hundreds of places. They have then plotted them on world maps, and drawn lines called isopleths (from the Greek *isos* meaning equal and *plethos* meaning quantity) to connect places with the same temperature, or rainfall, etc. These maps, which give us a good picture of climates over the whole world, have one feature in common: they reveal that climates are not scattered at random but fall into clearly distinguishable patterns.

The world's pattern of temperatures is formed of a

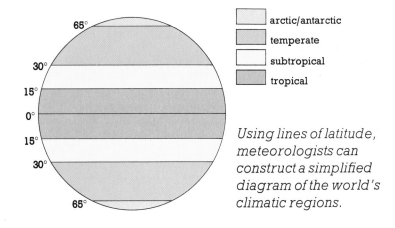

arctic/antarctic
temperate
subtropical
tropical

Using lines of latitude, meteorologists can construct a simplified diagram of the world's climatic regions.

series of zones whose boundaries are lines of latitude – the distance north or south of the Equator measured in degrees. The tropical zone, between about 15 degrees north and south, is the warmest part of the world. Average annual temperatures are above 77°F in many areas, and at Dallol in Ethiopia the average is 94°F, making it the hottest place on earth. Temperatures gradually decrease farther north or south of the Equator, and the coldest zones are the Arctic and Antarctic. The coldest place on earth, the so-called Pole of Cold, is Vostok in Antarctica, where an annual average of −72°F has been recorded.

The rainfall map is more complex but still shows a clearly recognizable pattern. There is a belt of heavy rainfall near the Equator, where many places get more than 80 inches per year. The subtropical zones, roughly 15 to 30 degrees north and south, are mostly very dry. In the northern subtropics, the Sahara and Arabian deserts have vast areas where the annual rainfall is less than four inches. However, subtropical parts of India and southeast Asia are just as wet as the equatorial regions.

In the southern subtropics there are deserts on the west sides of South America and Africa, and semi-desert stretches across much of Australia, but the east sides of all three continents are relatively wet. Most parts of the so-called temperate zones, between about 30 and 65 degrees north and south, get plenty of precipitation. However, some regions in western North America and the interior of Asia are semi-desert, mainly because they are sheltered from rain-bearing winds by high mountain ranges. The Arctic and Antarctic zones have relatively little precipitation, and most of it falls as snow.

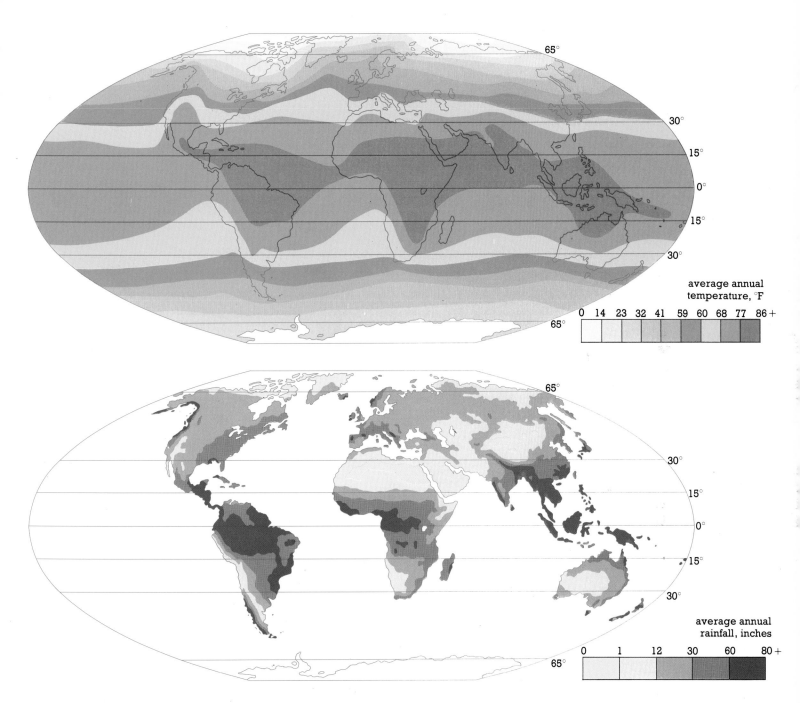

average annual
temperature, °F

0 14 23 32 41 59 60 68 77 86 +

average annual
rainfall, inches

0 1 12 30 60 80 +

*The world's average annual temperatures (top)
decrease toward the Poles. The presence of land
results in a northward and southward extension of the
hot equatorial zone, while the oceans have a cooling
influence. In contrast, the world's rainfall (below)
shows a complex pattern of wet and dry regions.
Because of the small number of observing stations,
measurements are not usually given for the Antarctic
and parts of the Arctic.*

Coastal Climates

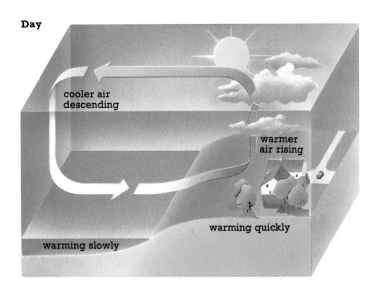

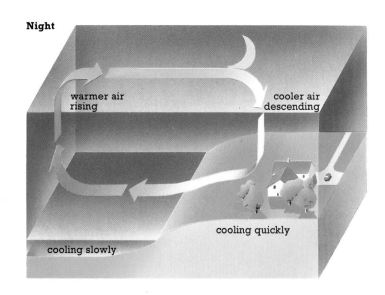

People visiting a sea coast often find that the weather is very different from the weather just a few miles inland. This is because coastlines are subject to variations on the general weather pattern of a region – variations which in the long term produce a clearly distinguishable coastal climate.

Suppose the day starts with a clear sky and no wind. Although equal amounts of sunshine fall on both the land and the sea, the surface of the sea heats up more slowly than the land surface, partly because more energy is needed to warm water and partly because the sun's heat is diffused several feet down into the water by the constant motion of waves and currents. The air above the sea is therefore cooler than the air over the land. The resulting temperature contrast causes a local circulation of air to develop. The light, warm air over the land rises and flows out toward the sea, while the colder heavier air over the sea flows to the land. A belt of clouds lying over the land may show where the air is rising, while skies will be clear over the sea, where the air is sinking.

The movement of the air can be felt as a cool sea breeze, which usually starts in the late morning, lasts through the afternoon and dies away in the evening. Although the breeze may be quite strong, it affects a layer of atmosphere only a few hundred feet deep, a fact that can be checked if there happen to be tall

These diagrams show typical wind circulations, actually very small monsoons, on a coast by day (at left) and by night (at right). Daytime winds from the ocean – or sea breezes – may penetrate up to 30 miles inland.

chimneys smoking near the shore. As the smoke rises, the sea breeze blows it inland. But higher up the smoke bends and blows out to sea, following the path of the light, warm air.

At night the wind circulation is reversed. Because the sun's heat has been dispersed through a layer of water several feet deep, the sea cools down more slowly than the land, and a breeze blows from the cooler land to the warmer sea.

These local circulations do not develop every day. For example, if the sky is cloudy, less of the sun's heat is able to reach the ground and as a result the temperature contrast is far less marked. Again, if there is a wind blowing over the whole region it will stir up the air and prevent a temperature contrast from developing.

Seas and large lakes also raise humidity levels in areas around their shores by giving off moisture to the air. In winter, when the waters tend to be much warmer than the adjacent land, they warm the air passing over them and sometimes cause a dramatic

A band of cold water off the coast of California has cooled the air blowing over it, forming this layer of low clouds. As the wind blows inland clouds burn away in the sunshine. Thus the coast has a much cooler and cloudier climate than places inland.

The map below of average annual snowfall (in inches) in the Great Lakes area, reveals highest levels south and east of the lakes. The arrow shows the prevailing wind direction in winter.

increase in precipitation. Some places to the east and south of the Great Lakes show this effect very clearly. Cold air blowing south from the Arctic becomes warmer and damper as it comes into contact with the water, then rises as it blows onto the upsloping shoreline. Places such as Buffalo, therefore, get heavy falls of snow due to the influence of the lake, and the adjacent land has an average of 90 to 140 days with snow on the ground every year.

In Europe, the North Sea is a major influence on the weather, especially in places bordering its west shore. Icy winds blow from the Soviet Union in winter with a temperature of 14°F or lower, and dry, sparkling clear air. As the air blows across the North Sea, it becomes warmer and picks up moisture. By the time these same winds reach the coast of eastern England, they produce very disagreeable weather conditions. It is often overcast and damp, with snow showers, and a much higher but in no way pleasant temperature of 30°F.

Mountain Climates

People who are taking a walk or bicycle ride in a mountainous area on a windless night often notice that the air temperature drops abruptly as they go downhill into a so-called pool of cold air. This odd phenomenon is a result of localized wind circulations that often develop in hilly or mountainous regions in clear weather.

If the mountain slopes are warmed by the sun in the morning, they, in turn, warm the air lying above them. This means that air in contact with the land surface at an altitude of, say 1000 feet, becomes warmer than air at the same altitude lying high above the valleys. The air above the mountains therefore rises, and clouds can develop as a result. If the atmosphere is unstable, these clouds may grow big enough to produce heavy showers in the afternoon. Meanwhile, the air sinks over the valleys. As it descends it becomes warmer, and any moisture it contains evaporates, producing dry, sunny weather. At night, the air nearest to the ground cools, and since cold air is denser than warm air it flows down the hillsides, collecting in a pool in the valleys.

Mountains also affect the winds and the weather in other ways. As air blows up and over a mountain range it cools as it rises. Therefore the side of a mountain range toward the wind, i.e., windward, will have cloudy weather in contrast to the side away from the wind, i.e., leeward, where the air sinks and produces clear weather. In the long term the windward side will have a wet climate, whereas the leeward side will lie in a dry "rain shadow." In the Hawaiian Islands, for example, the windward side of the mountains receives more than 300 inches of rain a year, while the leeward side in the rain shadow gets an average of 20 inches and is generally sunny.

Sometimes a warm, very dry wind, known in Alpine Europe as a Foehn, develops on the leeward side of a mountain range. Foehn winds often produce remarkable rises in temperature – as great as 46°F in the space of an hour – and may melt a thick layer of snow overnight. In the eastern Rockies the Foehn is known by its Indian name of chinook. There the wind may blow as a strong gale, hitting speeds of over 50 miles per hour.

Foehn winds probably have several causes, but the most important is the latent heat released by precipitation over mountains. Normally, air that cools as it

This diagram shows the typical sequence of breezes in a valley. Warming of the land surface by day causes air lying above it to rise (far left) while cooling by night causes air to flow down the slopes into a cold "pool" (below).

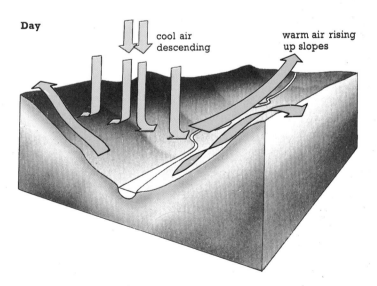

Day

cool air descending

warm air rising up slopes

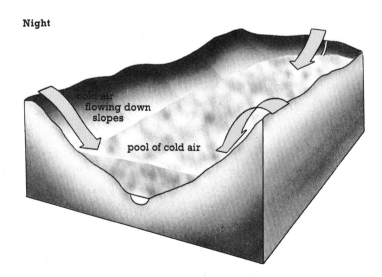

Night

cold air flowing down slopes

pool of cold air

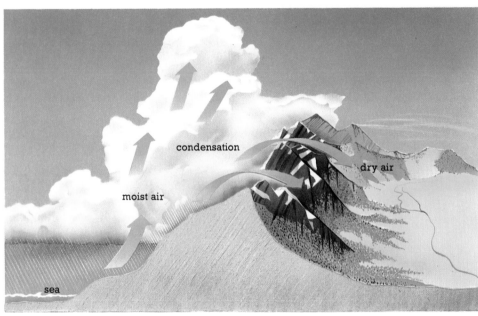

Early morning mist fills this valley, while surrounding uplands are clear. In the first part of the day, valley floors may average up to 7°F cooler than nearby hilltops.

Rain-bearing winds from the sea, crossing a coastal mountain range, release their moisture as they rise and cool. As a result the leeward side of the range receives relatively little rain and is said to lie in a "rain-shadow."

passes over a mountain reaches its original temperature when it returns to the height at which it started. If the rising air contains moisture, latent heat is released into the air as the moisture condenses to form clouds. If some of the water fell from the clouds as rain or snow, the heat that would have been used to turn it back to vapor again will remain in the descending air. The air will then become several degrees warmer than when it began its journey.

Monsoons

India, and some other countries in southern Asia, are said to have a monsoon climate, in which wet ocean winds blow onshore for almost half the year, and dry continental winds blow in the opposite direction for an equal period of time. In late spring, as the sun moves north, the Asian land mass heats up much more rapidly than the Indian Ocean. By May the land is hot and temperatures often reach 100°F or more. The difference in temperature between the continent and the ocean – as much as 18°F – sets up a gigantic circulation of air with warm air rising over the land while cooler air sinks over the ocean. Moist southwesterly air from the ocean rushes in to replace the rising air. Clouds build up, and rain starts pouring down, often accompanied by strong winds. The temperature drops to 80°F. Plants start growing rapidly, particularly rice, which is the chief source of nutrition in many areas.

Rainfall is particularly heavy on ranges of hills that run at right angles to the prevailing wind, causing the humid airstream to rise abruptly. The resulting rapid condensation creates some of the heaviest downpours in the world. Cherrapunji in northern India, at an altitude of 4308 feet, receives an annual average of 436 inches, and up to 139 inches have been recorded there in 15 days.

The rainy weather continues with only occasional breaks for three to four months. Eventually, in October, the rain dies away and is followed by a spell of warm, humid weather. Temperatures then gradually fall, until the land is much colder than the sea, and dry northeasterly winds flow out from the Asian continent across the Indian Ocean. This brings a winter of dry air, cloudless skies, and pleasant temperatures.

Although the monsoon brings plenty of rain to the west coast of India, in other parts of the country it sometimes fails, for reasons meteorologists do not yet fully understand. Crops cannot grow, and the people are faced with famine. Sometimes other parts of India can provide food, but in the worst years, when the monsoon fails completely over a large part of the country, thousands of people are threatened with starvation and other countries are

These maps show the path of the Asian monsoon as winds blow towards a low pressure zone over Asia in summer (below) and pour out from a high pressure zone in winter (below right).

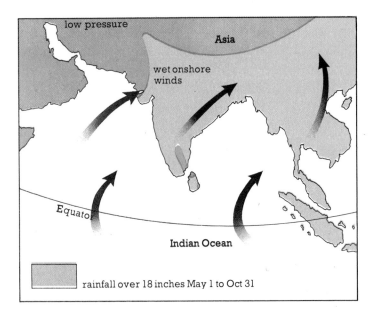

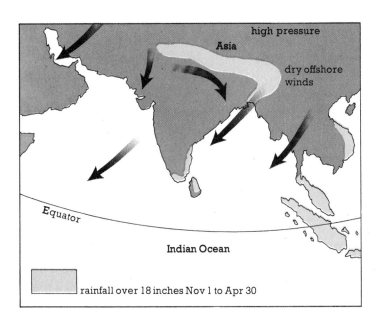

Heavy rain falls on a jungle road during the start of the monsoon season.

asked to send emergency supplies of grain.

The Asian summer monsoon is so powerful that it dominates other wind circulations and affects the weather in areas that are thousands of miles away from Asia. For example, strong northeasterly winds blow in the upper levels of the atmosphere above the monsoon. Meteorologists have suggested that some of the air rising over India gets caught up by these winds and is carried all the way to North Africa, where it sinks, producing clear skies. This suggests that the Asian monsoon may be helping to keep the Sahara a desert.

Monsoons also occur in northern Australia and parts of West Africa. Those continents are smaller than Asia so the temperature contrast is less marked, and as a result their monsoons are weaker and do not reach as far inland.

Meteorologists now use the term monsoon to include any wind system that covers both oceans and continental areas and blows from roughly opposite directions in winter and summer. This map shows that areas (blue) in which such systems occur, include not only India and southeast Asia but also parts of the Arabian desert and large areas of Africa.

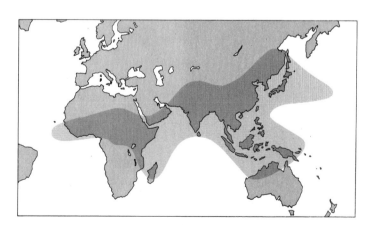

Climatic Variations

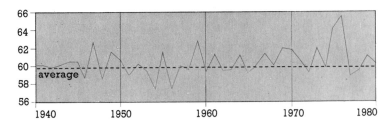

Average summer temperatures, England

Everyone has some idea of what an average winter is like, and soon notices if the winter weather is much colder or wetter than usual. But sometimes seasons of a particular type recur over several years, followed by a sequence of a different type. For example, a series of mild wet winters may be followed by a series of colder, drier winters. These sequences are called short-term climatic variations.

The winter temperatures in Atlanta, Georgia, in the eastern United States, have shown marked short-term variations. Every winter from 1949 to 1957 was warmer than previous averages, and several winters from 1958 to 1969 were colder. By contrast, in central England there have been only minor variations in summer temperatures. During the last 40 years, the cooler and warmer summers have been scattered

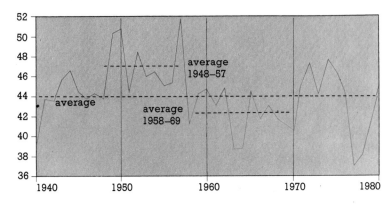

Average winter temperatures, Atlanta, Georgia

The charts above show that cyclical temperature fluctuations are more marked for Atlanta, Georgia, winters than for English summers.

The steadily decreasing annual rainfall between 1950 and 1973 in the Sahel (an arid strip of land along the southern border of the Sahara Desert) is highlighted here by healthy and withered grasses. The lower the rainfall for a year the more stunted the plant.

nearly at random. Although the two coolest summers, 1954 and 1956, were only two years apart, the intervening summer of 1955 was one of the warmest. The relatively warm summers of 1975 and 1976 were preceded and followed by several cooler summers.

Short-term climatic variations are of great importance to farmers, since if the climate becomes colder or wetter, a particular crop may not grow as well. Some strains of corn, for example, need four to five months to grow. If the growing season at a particular place is usually five months, and a climatic change occurs so that every month becomes only one degree colder, then the growing season could be reduced to four months and the corn crop might fail to ripen before the onset of fall.

Climatic variations affect rainfall amounts as well as temperature. In the Sahel region of West Africa, along the southern fringe of the Sahara Desert, the rainfall is usually just enough to produce grass for cattle. During the 1950s most years had above average rainfall. The area therefore became more fertile, and

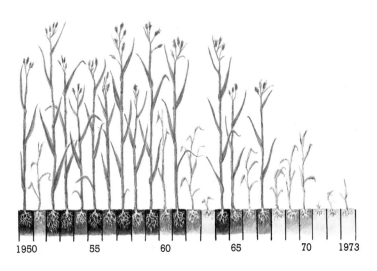

nomadic tribes moved more cattle into the area. Then the climate swung into a dry phase. From 1968 to 1973 every year had less rain than the average for the previous 30 years. Not enough grass grew for the large herds of cattle to live on, and at least 80 per cent died. Up to 200,000 people perished of starvation, and many others migrated to more fertile areas farther south.

In 1975–6 parts of Europe had a drought lasting 15 months. This was not nearly as long or tragic as the drought in the Sahel, but it still caused serious damage to crops, and resulted in water shortages in England and France. From May 1975 to August 1976 England received only half its normal rainfall. Reservoirs became very low and some dried up completely in the 1976 drought. Many crops shriveled in the dry

This photograph, taken at the height of the Sahel drought in 1973, shows skeletons of cattle strewn across the parched soil near a dried-up water hole.

soil. People were banned from watering their gardens or washing their cars, and England's usually green countryside became parched and brown.

The immediate cause of the European drought was an area of high-pressure air which persisted over the region. But meteorologists are still trying to discover why it remained stationary for so long. Some have suggested a link with ocean temperature in the area of the Cape Verde Islands 3000 miles to the south, but this theory can only be confirmed by further pains-taking research.

Climatic Correlations

In 1972 many regions had unusual weather. The Soviet Union's grain growing area suffered a serious drought, and European Russia had devastating forest fires. Temperatures reached 90°F for several days on the coast of the Arctic Ocean. In India and Bangladesh, the monsoon rains failed, causing widespread famine. A drought in the Sahel region of the southern Sahara was approaching its worst. Most of Australia was also hit by a drought. By contrast, a hurricane brought a week of rain and floods to the eastern United States, and Peru and the Philippines also had unusually heavy rains. The places worst hit by this weather were regions that grow a lot of grain. As a result, world stores of grain fell to dangerously low levels.

Unusual weather frequently occurs in different regions at the same time, and this highlights the fact that their climates may be directly connected.

One cause of such connections, known as correlations, is the jet stream. In the northern hemisphere, when the jet swings to the north, warm subtropical air flows farther north than usual. When it swings south, cold unsettled weather occurs farther south than usual. In 1972 a trough – a southward, low-pressure swing of the jet stream – lay over Britain, while a ridge – a high-pressure, northward swing – lay over the western Soviet Union. In 1976, however, the reverse situation was true, as illustrated by the pair of maps at the bottom of the opposite page.

Another correlation whose cause is known is the one between the climates of Australia and Peru. It results from a wind circulation in which warm air rises over the western Pacific and blows across the ocean to sink near the coast of Peru. This circulation was the reason why in 1972 Peru had rain and Australia had a drought, while in 1974 the reverse occurred.

The dried-up mud on the bottom of this English reservoir shows clearly the severity of the record-breaking drought of 1976.

In 1976 Moscow's severe downpours caused widespread flooding while England was desperately in need of rain.

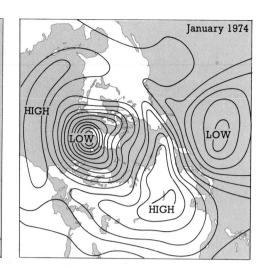

Contrasting winters in the northern hemisphere reveal strikingly different pressure patterns. In Europe, adjacent high- and low-pressure areas existed during January 1963, which was unusually cold. But January 1974 was mild, though windy.

The unusual weather of 1972 led many people to claim that climates everywhere had suddenly become worse. But this was not really the case. Sudden spells of severe weather had occurred before – for example, the winter of 1963 broke records for cold in both Europe and North America. Beginning in 1974, the rainfall in the Sahel region had gone back closer to normal, and both the United States and the Soviet Union also enjoyed a return to normal climates, with good harvests. India grew bumper crops in the summers from 1975 to 1978 as a result of heavy monsoon rains.

It was probably just an unfortunate coincidence that in 1972 many important crop-growing areas suffered from dry weather. Even so, climatic changes in some regions are undoubtedly related. For example, Britain had a cool cloudy summer in 1972 while the Soviet Union was having its drought. In the summer of 1976 the pattern was reversed. Britain suffered a heatwave, with hardly any rain, while in the Soviet Union an exceptionally wet summer produced record harvests.

Climatologists compare the changes of climate in many regions and try to find out which circulations influence them. This is the first clue to understanding climatic changes. They then study each circulation in detail, by trying to discover how the air moves, where it picks up its moisture, and where it drops it again as rain or snow, for example. In this way they are gradually learning more about why climate varies from place to place and from year to year.

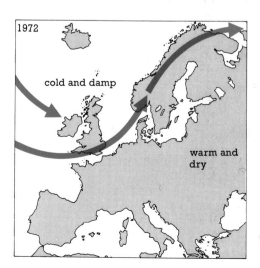

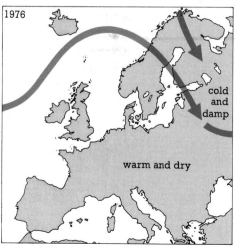

Meanders of the jet stream, as represented by the arrows in these diagrams, may have been responsible for contrasting weather in Britain and the Soviet Union in 1972 (far left) and 1976 (left).

Extreme Climates

Most of the world's population lives in a zone that is free from extremes of temperature and rainfall. Yet large tracts of the earth's land surface have such severe climates that humans cannot survive there without the protection of special clothing and houses.

Hot deserts are among the most inhospitable areas on earth. The air contains very little moisture, skies are nearly always cloudless, and less than four inches of rain fall each year. In summer, when the sun is overhead, the temperature can reach a scorching 125°F, but the nights are comparatively cool because the dry air loses heat very quickly. In winter the days are warm but not hot, and there may even be a frost at night. The largest desert is the Sahara in North Africa, but there are many others, for example the Gobi in Asia, the Atacama in Chile, and the Namib in southern Africa. Parts of the southwestern United States and much of Australia are classified as semi-desert. These are not quite as dry as true desert, but they have less than 12 inches of rain per year.

A desert is caused by low rainfall, not by extremes of temperature. Therefore, besides being some of the hottest places on earth deserts can also be some of the coldest. In the Antarctic interior, winter temperatures can plummet to −127°F, and summer days are rarely above freezing. The edge of the Antarctic is not as cold as the interior, due to the influence of the relatively warm ocean, but it is still a severe

The blistering sands and rock of Death Valley in California, where the average annual rainfall is only 1.7 inches. Such deserts have some of earth's most inhospitable climates.

Tropical rain forest in Costa Rica, showing the dense undergrowth that results from hot humid conditions where air temperatures are between 68°F and 95°F day and night throughout the year.

climate because of the strong, bitingly cold winds that blow much of the time. The climate in the other major ice desert, the Arctic, is less extreme than the Antarctic, although it is still very cold. Winter temperatures of −60°F are not uncommon.

Mountains always have colder climates than surrounding lowlands. High mountains in the temperate zone may even be as cold as the Arctic, with the additional hazard of gale-force winds. On the summit of Mount Washington in New Hampshire, at a height of 6262 feet, average temperatures range from 12°F in winter to 50°F in summer, and wind speeds average 35 miles per hour.

Mountain country near the Equator, by contrast, has a beautiful climate. For example, Quito in Ecuador, at 9222 feet, has a special kind of extreme climate – extremely agreeable. Temperatures range from 46°F at night to 72°F by day every month of the year. There are about four inches of rain per month

for nine months and the remaining three months stay dry. This has been called "the land of eternal spring."

Near the Equator, much of the land surface is covered by dense rain forest. Temperatures do not vary as much as they do in desert regions, staying close to 80°F throughout the year. Heavy rain falls nearly every day and the air is always very moist, creating a hothouse environment which is ideal for the growth of lush tropical plants. Trees, bushes, and smaller plants form a dense mass of foliage – often dripping with water – that is almost impossible to penetrate. Seen from above, the forest appears as a vast unbroken area of green foliage. Rain forests also provide a good habitat for hundreds of species of animals and insects, but the moist air produces a unpleasant "sticky heat" that most people find very uncomfortable.

The bleak mountains of Anvers Island, lying just off the Antarctic Peninsula at a latitude of 64½ degrees south, are permanently buried beneath a thick layer of snow and ice.

Mount Kilimanjaro in Tanzania spans two climatic extremes. While its crest is continually snow-covered average annual temperatures in the plains at its foot reach the mid-70s Fahrenheit.

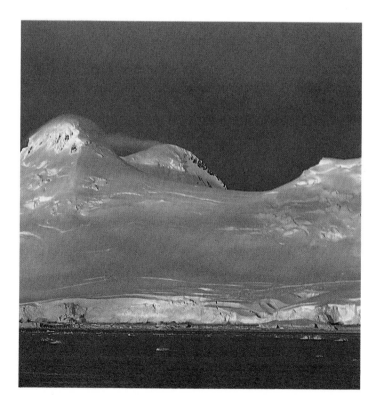

The Seasons

The seasons – spring, summer, fall, and winter – are caused by two phenomena: the earth revolves around the sun once a year, and the earth's axis tilts at an angle of 23.5 degrees.

From about March 21 to September 21 the northern hemisphere is tilted toward the sun, and so receives a greater input of heat than the southern hemisphere. On June 21, which is called the summer solstice, northern regions are tilted most directly toward the sun. At about that time, places in the northern temperate zone have long days and short nights, and the sun appears high in the sky at noon. In the Arctic zone during the summer, although the sun does not climb very high, it can be seen in the sky for the whole 24 hours of the day, so that in regions such as northern Norway and northern Alaska the sun remains just above the horizon at midnight, a phenomenon known as the "midnight sun."

During the other half of the year, the northern hemisphere is tilted away from the sun, and receives less heat than the southern hemisphere. At about the

The earth is tilted at an angle of 23.5 degrees relative to the direct rays of the sun. This means that in the course of a year the area directly exposed to the sun's rays migrates north and south of the Equator, resulting in seasonal temperature variations.

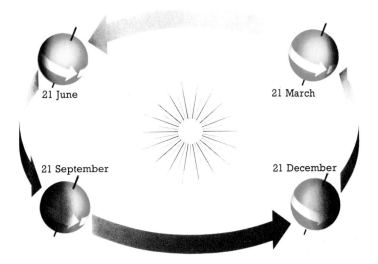

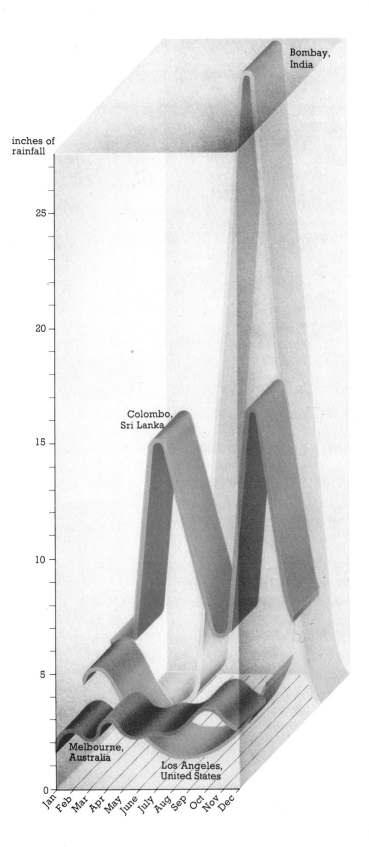

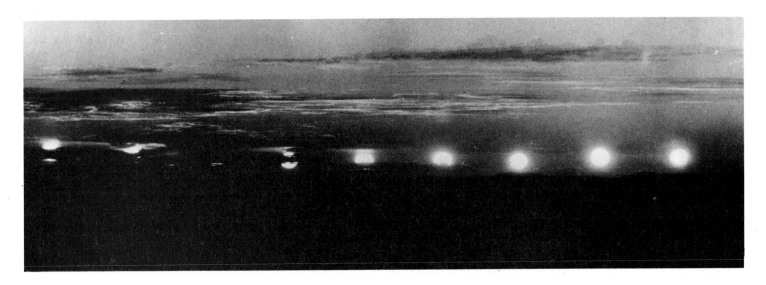

time of the winter solstice on December 21, the sun rises late in the northern temperate zone, passes low to the south, and sets early. In the Arctic zone at this time the sun does not rise at all, and it is dark all day.

In the southern hemisphere the daylight patterns are reversed. The winter solstice is around June 21 when, in the southern temperate zone, the sun is low to the north, and in the antarctic zone it is dark all day. There the summer solstice is about December 21.

In regions near the Equator the seasons are less marked, so that in the tropical zone the sun always climbs high in the sky, and the length of the day varies only slightly during the year.

Halfway between the solstices, on days called equinoxes, the sun passes directly overhead at the Equator, so that all places on earth have 12 hours of day and 12 hours of night. In the northern hemisphere the spring equinox falls about March 21, the autumn equinox about September 21. These dates are, of course, reversed in the southern hemisphere.

The cycle of sunshine obviously has a major effect on temperature – but not quite the one that might be expected. In the northern hemisphere it might be imagined that the weather would be warmest about June 21, the time of the summer solstice. However, because the earth takes time to warm up,

This multiple exposure photograph shows the path of the midnight sun as it travels along the polar horizon just before and after midnight on June 21.

the warmest period, on the average, is about a month later, in mid-July. Records of the weather show that the warmest months in the northern temperate zone are June, July, and August. Meteorologists usually refer to these months as summer, and define fall as September to November, winter as December to February, and spring as March to May. But these divisions are only made so that it is easier to work out averages and compare one year with another. Hot weather can occur in April, snow can fall in May, and the temperature goes up and down many times in the course of a year. Spring weather does not really begin on March 1 – it comes in fits and starts, at any time from February to April.

In many parts of the world rainfall also changes with the seasons. The belts of wet and dry weather move north in the northern summer and south in the southern summer. As a result, some places, such as California and Spain, are in a rainy belt in winter and in a dry belt in summer. Los Angeles gets very little rain in summer but moderate amounts in winter, whereas Bombay gets almost all its rain in summer and none in winter. Colombo, in Sri Lanka, has rainy seasons in spring and fall because the equatorial rain belt passes over it twice. Melbourne's rainfall does not vary greatly throughout the year, although winter is the driest season, on average.

The graph at left shows four contrasted patterns of rainfall. Places receiving similar annual totals may show quite different patterns of rainfall distribution through the year.

37

The Daily Weather

This white carpet of frost results from heat lost by radiation from the earth on a clear, calm night. It consists of millions of minute needle-shaped ice-crystals, formed when tiny droplets of water vapor come into contact with the frozen ground.

Day

Night

These diagrams show how the earth gains and loses heat by day and by night. Orange arrows show heat coming directly from the sun, or reflected off clouds and the earth. Yellow arrows show heat radiated from the earth. Where clouds occur at night, some of the radiant heat is deflected back toward the earth, while some escapes through the clouds to continue rising.

The regular cycle of day and night creates the most important of all weather variations. The sun is continually radiating heat, which falls on the earth by day, warming the ground and the atmosphere lying above it. At any particular place on earth, the higher the sun is in the sky, the more heat that place normally receives because the sun's rays are concentrated over a smaller area. At the same time, the earth is continually radiating heat out into space, so that by night the land surface becomes increasingly cold. The difference between heat received and heat radiated is known as the radiation balance, and it is this which determines daily variations in temperature. However, the air takes time to warm up or cool down, and so is warmest in mid-afternoon, not at noon.

Humidity also goes through a daily cycle. Suppose the air at dawn is saturated with moisture (100 per cent humidity). As the temperature rises, the humidity falls, perhaps to about 60 per cent by 3 p.m. The humidity then rises again during the evening and night as the air cools. The next night the temperature may fall more quickly, so that the humidity reaches 100 per cent by midnight. As the temperature goes on falling, some of the moisture has to condense, and because the ground cools more rapidly than the air, the water first condenses on the ground as dew. If the ground temperature is below the freezing point, at 32°F the moisture turns to crystals of ice, which form a white covering of frost. If there is a slight breeze, the layer of air immediately above the cold land surface is cooled as well, and mist or fog forms.

When the sky is cloudy, the radiation balance changes. The clouds deflect away some of the sun's radiation by day, so the ground does not get so warm. At night, however, the layer of cloud acts as an insulator, reflecting some of the earth's radiation back to the ground and preventing it getting so cold. This is why, in cloudy weather, the air is usually cooler by day and warmer by night than in clear weather.

Clouds

Clouds provide a weather spectacle that people have always watched with fascination. Although, in scientific terms, all clouds are nothing more than airborne accumulations of condensed water vapor, in everyday life they present infinitely changeable patterns, often of remarkable beauty. Shafts of sunlight piercing through clouds or seen in the closing minutes of a thunderstorm have inspired poets and painters since the dawn of civilization. The sudden appearance of gray, rainladen clouds has ruined outdoor events the world over. The unexpected formation of great storm clouds has spelled death for thousands of sailors and mountaineers, caught far from shelter.

To both meteorologists and amateur weatherwatchers, the shape, color, and altitude of clouds provide invaluable clues to the kind of weather that can be expected over the next few hours or days. An English chemist, Luke Howard, published a paper in 1804 that provides the names, still in use today, of the three basic cloud types: *cirrus* (Latin for curl of hair), *cumulus* (heap) and *stratus* (spread out). As the photographs at right show, the names were aptly chosen. In the years since, the names have been combined and expanded to describe the combinations and mutations of the basic types.

Cirrus clouds most commonly occur at high altitudes (16,500–45,000 feet). Their gauzy drawn out shapes and trailing wisps are a sign of strong winds that may be bringing a change in the weather. Cumulus clouds include puffy, fairweather clouds and larger heaps of clouds which sometimes give light showers. They tend to form at middle altitudes of about 1500–6500 feet above ground level. The characteristically low-altitude stratus brings light rains. And though no cloud can be regarded as an infallible prophet, the towering cumulonimbus, whose base may be under 1000 feet above the ground while its crown may reach 40,000 feet, should be respectfully heeded as an almost unerring indication of thunder.

The sunlit billows of this large area of cumulus clouds suggest a period of good weather.

A cumulonimbus, relieved of its rain, stretches across the sky. Other cloud types are pictured below.

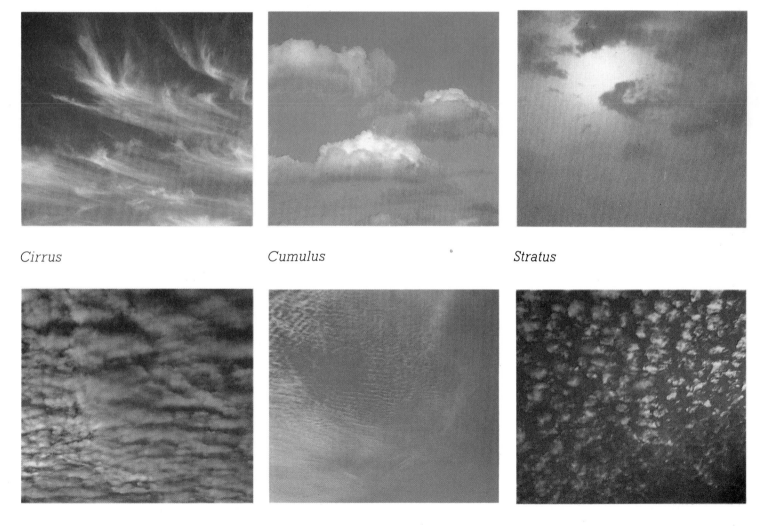

Cirrus

Cumulus

Stratus

Stratocumulus

Cirrocumulus

Altocumulus

Thunder and Lightning

Thunder and lightning are always associated with tall cumulonimbus clouds, in which there are strong currents of rising and falling air. Meteorologists are unsure of the precise cause of lightning, but it is probable that contact between raindrops or ice crystals, as they rise and fall within a cloud, produces build-ups of static electricity similar to those that sometimes cause crackling in our clothes when we undress.

Electricity builds up in our clothing by friction with our skin, which produces a positive charge on one and a negative charge on the other. In the case of lightning, the lower part of the cumulonimbus cloud becomes negatively charged, while other parts – and the ground below the cloud – become positively charged. These charges gradually accumulate until, eventually, they become so strong that the air cannot hold them and they are discharged in a giant spark – a lightning flash. The air through which this spark travels becomes intensely hot and expands violently and it is this explosive expansion that produces a clap of thunder. The sound waves then bounce back and forth between the ground and the clouds, producing the rumble of thunder that follows the clap. Some flashes occur between one part of the cloud and another, while others go between the cloud and the ground.

Vast amounts of energy are locked up in thunderstorms. When lightning strikes the ground, this energy is released in a heat burst of up to 54,000°F – five times hotter than the surface of the sun. People can survive being struck by lightning if the path of the electric charge misses their brain and heart.

If lightning strikes close by, a loud clap of thunder will be heard at the same time. But if it strikes farther away, there will be an interval between the lightning

In a typical thunder cloud, lightning leaps at about 87,000 miles per second between negative electric charges at the base and positive charges at the top and on the ground. The accompanying clap of thunder may be heard as far as 40 miles away.

and the thunder. The reason for this is that whereas light travels at 186,282 miles per second, sound waves travel on average at a mere 1056 feet per second. An observer can tell how far away a thunderstorm is by measuring the time between the lightning and the first clap of thunder: the distance is about one mile for each five seconds of the waiting period.

Lightning tends to discharge itself through the highest point available. The most dangerous place to be in a thunderstorm is in an open space on top of a hill, or under an isolated tree. Trees are particularly vulnerable to lightning since their moist interiors are excellent conductors of electricity. An estimated 10,000 fires are started in this way every year in the United States. The safest place to be during a thunderstorm is in a low building, or in a car. When lightning strikes a car the metal body acts as a protective cage, causing electric charges to travel across its surface and pass into the ground over the tires.

People sometimes say that lightning never strikes twice in the same place, but this is not true. Tall buildings may be struck by lightning up to ten times in a year. They can be protected with a lightning rod – a pointed metal rod mounted on the roof, with a cable leading down to a metal plate buried in the ground. The conductor attracts the electricity but then conducts it harmlessly away.

Thunderstorms are most likely to happen when the

lower atmosphere is warm and moist, and the upper atmosphere is cold, conditions that encourage strong rising air currents to develop. They are particularly frequent in the equatorial zone, where some places get them on more than 200 days a year. At this moment about 1800 thunderstorms are happening in the world, and about eight million flashes of lightning occur every day.

If a radio is on when lightning flashes, it makes a crackle because the large amounts of static electricity interfere with the radio waves. Meteorologists use this phenomenon to locate storms. Using sensitive radio aerials two observers perhaps 500 miles apart establish the direction of a flash and then exchange their readings by telephone or radio. The point at which the flash occurred can then be worked out by plotting both directions on a map. However meteorologists more commonly detect and track thunderstorms over a smaller area, say within a 150-mile radius. They do this by using radar to give a map of the storm on the radar screen as the radio waves bounce off the raindrops.

The branch of this oak tree has been shattered by lightning that has traveled down the best conducting path: moist layers of wood lying just beneath the bark.

Lightning strikes the Eiffel Tower in a blinding electric storm over Paris. A single stroke may carry a current of up to 100,000 amps.

Rain, Snow and Hail

Everyone knows what it is like to see rain pouring from a cloudy, gray sky. But, luckily, most of us live in areas that receive only moderate amounts of precipitation and we know that usually it will not last long. Other areas are very wet: Mount Waialeale in Hawaii has an average yearly rainfall of 451 inches – over ten times New York's average of 42 inches. while Cherrapunji in India averages 436 inches a year, making it the second wettest place on earth.

When a cloud reaches the cold, upper levels of the atmosphere, ice crystals start to form. These crystals increase in size as invisible water vapor condenses directly onto them, and gradually they turn into snow crystals. The snow crystals fall slowly through the cloud, picking up more moisture and sticking to other crystals to form snowflakes. When these small white bundles of crystals – usually about half an inch in diameter – reach the ground, they quickly cover it with a soft layer of snow. If the air temperature at ground level is more than about 40°F, the snowflakes will melt on the way down and fall to the ground as rain. If only some of them melt, the precipitation is called sleet.

Not all precipitation forms in this way. Sometimes very small water droplets form in clouds. When the droplets start falling toward the bottom of the cloud, the air resistance is great in proportion to their size, so they travel very slowly. But as they fall, the droplets collide with each other and combine, forming bigger drops. These are heavy enough to overcome the air resistance, and they fall more quickly, sweeping up more droplets and becoming bigger still. The deeper the cloud, the bigger the drops become, until eventually they fall out of the bottom of the cloud and down to the ground as rain.

Because cumulonimbus clouds contain strong up-currents of air, any raindrops caught inside them are carried rapidly upward. If the drops rise sufficiently high, they freeze into tiny pellets of ice. Although

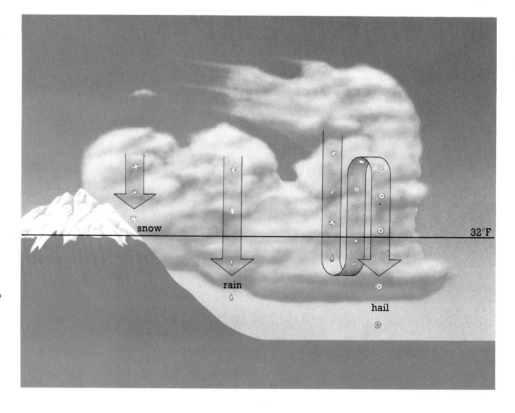

This diagram shows the conditions that favor snow (left), rain (center) and hail (right). The formation of hailstones depends on the presence of strong upcurrents of air that lift a falling raindrop back into the cloud, where it freezes and then receives a skin of frozen water vapor.

Snow crystals come in an endless variety of fragile shapes. Shown here are, left, two crystals known as stellars, with radiating limbs and, above, a more solid crystal called a plate.

Raindrops vary a great deal in size. However, they are never larger in diameter than about $\frac{1}{5}''$, about the size of the largest drops shown in the leaf above. Beyond this size individual raindrops split into smaller droplets.

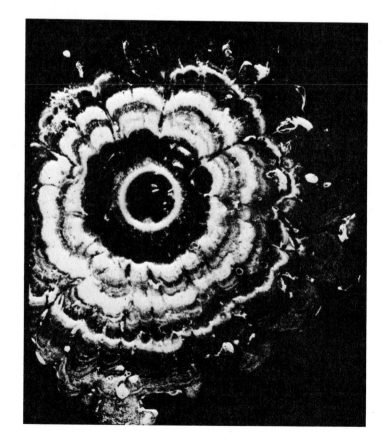

A cross-section of a hailstone shows layers of ice radiating out from the center like rings in a tree-trunk. As many as 25 distinct layers have been found on a single hailstone.

upcurrents eventually weaken, these pellets often fall into other upcurrents and collide with suspended water droplets, gaining a coating of water that will freeze as they are carried upward again. This may happen several times, so the frozen raindrops get coated with several layers of ice. Eventually the pellets become so heavy that they plunge through the upcurrents and fall to the ground as hailstones.

Hailstones can do enormous damage to crops and fragile buildings such as greenhouses. Larger hailstones have even been known to dent cars. The largest hailstone recorded, at Coffeyville in Kansas, was over seven inches in diameter. A hailstorm in Alberta, Canada, in 1953 poured hailstones over more than 650 square miles, destroying plants and killing thousands of birds – their skulls smashed by hail the size of golf balls.

Fog and Smog

Fog has exactly the same composition as clouds, a collection of tiny water droplets suspended in the air. The only difference between them is that clouds form when air rises and cools to its saturation point; fog forms when air near the ground cools and becomes saturated.

Fog forms most commonly on a cloudless night when the ground loses heat rapidly. As the ground gets colder, it cools the air above. If the air is still, only the bottom few feet of air cool, and there will be no fog, or only a ground fog. But if there is a slight breeze, the cooling is spread through a layer of 30 to more than 300 feet deep, and fog forms throughout the layer. If there is a strong breeze or a layer of clouds, the air will not cool to its saturation point, and there will be no fog. In fact, it is very difficult to predict whether there will be fog on a particular night, and even if fog does form, a slight increase in wind or clouds may suddenly disperse it.

In hill or mountain country the colder, heavier air drains downhill at night and collects in the hollows. As a result, fog forms at night in the valleys while the hills remain clear. In temperate regions fog is most common in fall and winter, when the air is relatively moist and nights are long. It usually occurs during periods of high pressure when winds tend to be light and skies clear. Fog that occurs on high hills is really just a layer of low clouds. However, most fog disperses during the daytime as the sun warms the air, and as winds may spring up. But if the layer of fog is thick, the sun and wind may not be strong enough to disperse it completely, and it may become even thicker the next night.

Fog often forms over the sea, for example, when warm, humid air blows over a cold ocean. Sometimes the fog may be carried inland for several miles before dispersing. Fog is particularly common along the northeast coast of the United States and Newfoundland, where it is caused by warm, wet winds blowing

The Golden Gate Bridge which spans the vast expanse of open water, San Francisco Bay, rises above a dense white bank of rolling sea fog.

off the Gulf Stream across the colder northern waters.

Dust or fine moisture particles in the air cause haze, in which visibility is reduced to a mile or so. The air is often hazy near industrial areas and such pollution can drift for hundreds of miles. For example, during long spells of easterly winds England gets haze caused by pollution drifting over from Belgium and Germany. There are other forms of haze caused by fine sand, forest fires, or the gas-producing photochemical reaction from trees in a forest. Any land surface adds its share of foreign particles to the atmosphere, so that air blowing from a continent is often hazier than air blowing from an ocean.

Smog is a mixture of smoke and fog. It may be dangerous not only because it reduces visibility but also because the smoke may contain chemicals, such as sulfur, which can damage health when inhaled. Cities that once burned a lot of coal used to get "pea-soup" smogs, so called because they were a dirty yellow color and very dense. About 4000 people died of chest and lung diseases such as bronchitis during a pea-soup smog in London from December 5 to 9, 1952. However, in many cities people are no longer allowed to burn smoky coal, and smogs from coal smoke are now rare. Also, areas likely to be affected by smog can now be pinpointed by analyzing the local geography and weather conditions.

This enables industrial pollution to be more strictly controlled.

The worst type of smog is photochemical smog, which is unfortunately becoming more common. It occurs in hot, sunny weather when chemicals produced by car exhaust fumes are changed by sunlight into substances that are both unpleasant and dangerous to health. One of the worst examples of photochemical smog in the world occurs in Los Angeles, a very large city with an enormous number of cars, which gets a great deal of sunshine in summer. Exhaust gases do not disperse because the winds are light and the city is half surrounded by mountains. When pressure is high, a layer of warm air a few hundred feet above the ground acts like a lid, sealing in the pollution.

Industrial pollution forms a filthy smog over Santiago, Chile. The yellowish tinge is due to the presence of sulfur dioxide.

Windstorms
and Heatwaves

Very strong winds occur in hurricanes and tornadoes, but they can also occur for other reasons. In the deep low-pressure areas of temperate latitudes, winds often reach gale force, 40 miles per hour, and even hurricane force, 75 miles per hour. Gale-force winds often blow in coastal areas, where they are a hazard to crews of fishing boats and workers on oil rigs. Oil and construction companies find it worthwhile to employ meteorologists to make continuous forecasts for them.

On January 2–3, 1976 a deep low-pressure area moving east from the Atlantic produced winds up to 116 miles per hour across much of Europe. About 100,000 trees blew down in Britain alone, towns were isolated for several hours and electricity supplies to some places were cut for several days. The death toll in Europe reached 64, and though the effects of the storms were worst on land, damage was also done at sea: in Denmark six fishing boats were sunk and a trawler was lost off the Dutch coast. This was one of the worst European windstorms since 1703, when a similar storm killed 8000 people at sea.

Sometimes mountains can cause freak winds in a limited area. For example, Boulder, Colorado, has severe windstorms several times a year. Boulder is on the leeward side of the Rockies and is usually sheltered from the westerly gales which prevail in that region. However, when there is a layer of stable air higher up in the atmosphere, air rises over the windward side of the mountains and pours down the leeward side like water over a cliff.

A spell of unusually warm weather is called a heatwave. In the summer of 1976 Britain's weather was dominated by powerful high-pressure systems. This resulted in an exceptional heatwave and temperatures reached 90°F on 16 successive days. In the summer of 1980 parts of Texas reported temperatures over 100°F for more than 30 consecutive days. If someone from Texas had been in Britain he would have called the heatwave just a pleasantly warm spell! In Death Valley, California, a temperature of

A crane rests entangled in a mass of twisted scaffolding after collapsing in freak winds that raged through Sheffield, England, in 1962.

120°F has been recorded on 43 successive days.

In many regions in latitudes from 30 to 40 degrees north and south – for example, on the coast of California and in southern Australia – summer is a hot, dry season, with temperatures reaching 100°F. Most plants shrivel up, leaving a mass of tinder-dry vegetation that presents a major fire risk. Although legislation can reduce the risk of fires being started by human carelessness, it is very difficult to control the most frequent cause of bush and forest fires – lightning. Even though only three to five per cent of lightning fires burn out of control they can cause colossal damage, engulfing up to 1000 acres in 30 minutes. A forest fire in California in 1970 destroyed 175,000 acres of vegetation and 382 buildings, and killed 5 people, while a fire in Australia in 1952 killed 110,000 sheep in seven and a half hours.

In this South African bush fire flickering sheets of flame sweep across a blackened landscape and threaten to engulf wooden houses.

Downpours and Floods

Normally rain does not last more than a few hours, since it is produced by a low-pressure area or front which moves on and gives way to clearer weather. Occasionally, though, a low stays in one place for several days and drops continuous, heavy rain onto the areas under it. When this happens the ground becomes saturated with water and rivers begin to rise, sometimes bursting their banks and flooding low-lying land in surrounding areas.

In January 1974, an almost stationary area of low pressure gave eastern Australia its wettest month on record. Large areas near Brisbane received more than 20 inches of rain in the last week of January alone, and some places got 50 inches in a week! Ten thousand homes were damaged or destroyed, coal mines and factories were flooded, and untreated sewage mixed with the floodwaters. The total cost of the flood damage in Queensland was estimated to be more than 100 million dollars.

When rain is extremely heavy and all the water starts to drain away at once, a sudden, violent flood called a flash flood occurs. Flash floods are most often caused by thunderstorms that remain in one place for several hours. They can happen anywhere, but their effects are worst in narrow mountain valleys.

In June 1972 torrential rains on the slopes of the Black Hills in South Dakota caused catastrophic flash

The weather map for January 31, 1953 when a severe depression over the North Sea caused catastrophic floods in neighboring countries. The large white arrow shows the direction of the storm tide, the smaller arrows indicate wind direction.

This aerial photograph shows just one of 67 major breaches of dikes (marine levees) in The Netherlands during the floods of 1953. Nearly half of the dikes were damaged along a line of almost 450 miles.

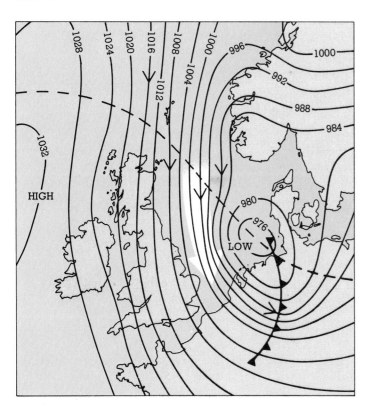

flooding along a twelve-mile stretch of Rapid Creek, which flows through Rapid City. The death toll there reached 238 and more than a hundred million dollars' worth of damage was caused.

A catastrophic flash flood occurred on August 15, 1952 at Lynmouth in southwest England, a village lying at the foot of a gorge that runs down to the sea. That night a torrential thunderstorm raged in the hills above the village, bringing eight inches of rain in a few hours. Floodwaters roared down the narrow valley at almost 20 miles per hour, carrying tree trunks, telephone poles, and enormous boulders. The village was devastated. Several buildings and many cars were washed into the sea, 23 people were killed and one thousand were made homeless.

Many of the world's major rivers have man-made dams and embankments called levees along their length which hold back sudden buildups of water and help to prevent floods. Just how important these are was brought home to the people of Kansas City in 1951 when the Kansas River – which lacked levees at some points – burst its banks after torrential rain and caused one of the most disastrous floods in the United States in modern times. About 2500 homes were lost, with damages of 870 million dollars.

Some floods are caused by stormy weather over the sea. In January 1953 a low moved across the North Sea toward Denmark. Northerly gales behind the low pushed water ahead of the wind. The effect of this displaced water was made worse by an abnormally high tide. The buildup of water breached sea defenses in eastern England, and the sea rushed inland, drowning 307 people. In The Netherlands the flood was an even greater disaster, with 1700 people drowned and over 50,000 evacuated from flooded homes.

The remains of a wooden house lie smashed on a bridge parapet, following floods that devastated Big Thompson Canyon in northern Colorado in August 1976.

Blizzards
and Ice Storms

The effects of heavy snowfall are often very severe. Livestock may freeze to death in open fields. Roads between towns can be closed by drifts. In cities, four inches of snow can snarl traffic and six inches is enough to bring some railroads to a standstill.

Just how dramatic the effects of heavy snow can be was demonstrated to New Yorkers in the winters of 1977 and 1978. The blizzards in January 1977 brought a high death toll. Many of these deaths were a result not of cold but of heart attacks while snow-clearing, or asphyxiation from exhaust fumes as motorists sat in their stranded cars. Buffalo, in New York State, lay under drifts 20 to 30 feet high, and had a total winter snowfall of 183.1 inches – 57 inches above the previous record set in 1909–10. Thousands of tons of snow and ice had to be transferred into trucks and railroad cars and dumped in areas where it could melt without risk of flooding.

Conditions were just as appalling in New York in 1978, when one February day brought one of the heaviest 24-hour periods of snow on record – a

A car crawls along a road invisible beneath drifting snow during a blizzard in the Faeroe Islands in the North Atlantic.

staggering 18 inches. On the Long Island Expressway an estimated 3000 stranded cars blocked the paths of snowplows. The weight of snow broke the roofs of more than a dozen buildings.

Heavy snowfalls bring the hazard of flooding when the snow melts. In England in March 1947, after the snowiest winter since 1814, warm air brought heavy rain and strong winds. Temperatures rose from below freezing to 45°F in a few hours. Snow still lying on the ground melted rapidly, but the frozen ground stopped the water from draining away, so it stayed on the surface. As a result, vast lakes formed all over the countryside and rivers overflowed. At Selby in Yorkshire, 70 per cent of the houses were flooded. Floods like this occur every year in parts of Iceland. As snow melts in the mountains in spring, rivers may become several miles wide, reshaping the land surface over which they flow. When the rivers subside, their beds may have moved a mile from where they were before.

Ice storms occur frequently in the United States. These are caused by raindrops or melted snow reaching a ground surface with a temperature below freezing point. The raindrops freeze as soon as they touch anything and roads and pavements become coated with a layer of smooth, clear ice called glaze. Ice can build up quickly on telephone wires or the branches of trees, and become heavy enough to break them. Portland, Oregon, suffered from a typical winter ice storm in January 1979. There, the weight of ice brought down trees, which fell across powerlines and broke cables, cutting off electricity supplies for several hours.

Plane trees beside Lake Geneva are seen here (right) festooned with ice after high winds whipped up 20-foot high clouds of spray in freezing temperatures.

Hurricanes

Hurricanes are very intense areas of low pressure, from 100 to 300 miles across, which originate in areas where there are plentiful supplies of warm, moist air. They usually breed in tropical and subtropical regions in both hemispheres at 5–25 degrees latitude over oceans that are warmer than about 80°F. The moist air spins into the center of the low-pressure area with ever-increasing speed and rises in the storm. As the air rises, the moisture it has collected condenses, producing dense clouds and extremely heavy rain. Latent heat released by the moisture then makes the air rise still faster until it spins away, outward from the top of the storm.

Once formed, hurricanes can keep themselves going for many days by sucking in new supplies of warm, moist air. They usually drift westward in both hemispheres because they occur in zones where winds tend to be from the east, although their movements from one day to the next may be irregular and difficult to forecast. Eventually, some of them strike land. When a hurricane moves over land, its supply of moisture is cut off, and as a result, it starts decaying – that is, air starts filling up the low pressure at the center. The winds then drop to about 60 miles per hour, but extremely heavy rains continue for several days because the air is still rising rapidly.

In the center of every hurricane, surprisingly, there is a circular area of very low pressure with

From above, hurricanes – or typhoons, as they are called in the Pacific – look like vast whirlpools of clouds. This storm, photographed from Apollo 9, swirls over the Pacific Ocean.

Hurricane winds of up to 180 miles per hour blast palm trees and whip up stinging clouds of sand at Miami Beach, Florida.

This village in the Dominican Republic was virtually wiped out when Hurricane Inez moved across the Caribbean in October 1966.

light winds and clear skies – the eye of the storm. Because a hurricane is circular in shape, winds blow in opposite directions on either side of the eye. People caught in a hurricane find that after the winds have howled for several hours from one direction they die down, creating a deceptive calm that is really only a brief interval occurring as the eye passes overhead. After an hour or less, the winds on the other side of the hurricane arrive, blowing just as violently as they did from the opposite direction.

Hurricanes that hit land are some of the most destructive of weather systems, causing immense damage to buildings and crops and sometimes wiping out entire towns and villages. The devastation results not only from the wind, but also from extremely heavy rains, and stormsurges as high as 25 feet which sweep inland from the sea. In November 1970 a hurricane in the densely populated Ganges Delta region of East Pakistan killed 300,000 people according to the official reports, and up to a million according to unofficial estimates. It also caused severe food shortages by devastating the coastal fishing industry.

Every year six or more hurricanes develop in the warm, tropical North Atlantic. Two or three of these cause havoc as they pass over some of the Caribbean islands or strike the east coast of the United States. The entire United States coastline from Texas to Maine is liable to be affected by the full force of hurricanes, and lowland areas anywhere east of the Rockies can suffer floods from hurricanes that carry violent rainstorms inland.

Another breeding ground for hurricanes is the tropical Pacific region. These storms affect the Philippines, China, and Japan, where they are known as typhoons. Other regions likely to be affected include India and Bangladesh in the northern hemisphere, and the Malagasy Republic and northern Australia in the southern, where such storms are known as cyclones.

Tornadoes

Tornadoes, like hurricanes, are whirling masses of air, with intensely low pressure at the center. In other ways, tornadoes are totally different. A tornado is rarely more than 880 yards across, yet in spite of its smaller size, it can be even more violent than a hurricane. Winds of 206 miles per hour have been measured, but they may well reach twice this speed. Reliable measurements have not been made, because a tornado passing over an anemometer – the instrument used to measure wind speed – usually wrenches it from its stand.

Tornadoes are caused by a strong uplift of air, which sucks in the lower air and makes it spin faster and faster, just like a very slender hurricane. In the atmosphere the air usually spins cyclonically, that is, counterclockwise in the northern hemisphere and clockwise in the southern.

Tornadoes are most likely to occur when the lower air is warm and moist, and a higher layer of air is cold and dry. In these conditions strong upward currents of air often develop, and then a violent squall line. As the lower air rises its moisture condenses as clouds and releases latent heat, making it even more

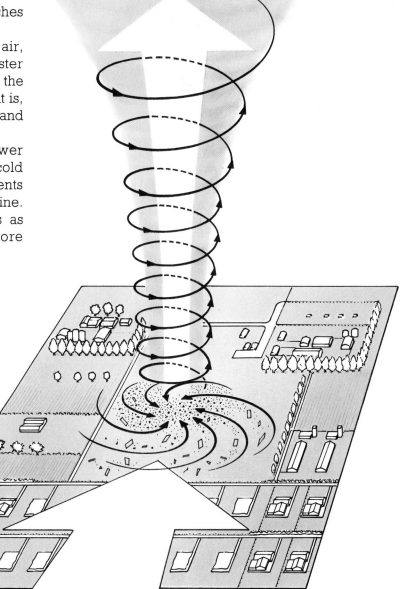

This diagram shows the inward spiral motion of the wind flow in a tornado. Moist tropical air rushes in at the base, to the low pressure center, at speeds of up to 150 miles per hour. Midwest tornadoes have been recorded over 880 yards wide.

buoyant so that it rises even faster. These conditions are common in the American Midwest where warm moist air flows north from the Gulf of Mexico, while cold dry air flows over the top of it. When the warm air starts rising, the situation is explosive, and severe thunderstorms and tornadoes soon develop.

An approaching tornado appears as a tall, funnel-shaped menacing cloud. There is often heavy rain with thunder and lightning, and hail not far away. As the tornado gets nearer people hear a deep roar, which gets louder and louder. They should quickly take refuge in as low a shelter as possible, preferably a cellar. Tornadoes may suck up anything in their paths, including people, animals, and even small buildings, carry them for hundreds of yards, and then send them plummeting to the ground.

The low pressure in the eye of the tornado can also create a dramatic difference in pressure between the outside and inside of buildings, whose interiors may remain at normal air pressure. After a tornado, houses sometimes appear to have exploded, with their walls and windows blown out. Although the damage can be severe and people may be killed, the track of the tornado is narrow. House roofs on one side of a road can be lifted off, while houses on the other side are untouched.

The Midwest has by far the worst tornadoes in the world. There they travel up to nearly 300 miles and may completely destroy half a town. Most houses in the worst affected states have basements or underground cellars in which people can shelter. But the chance of any particular house being hit is very small, and many people in the Midwest have never seen a tornado.

The ominous funnel of a tornado is pictured here twisting its way across central Kansas. The funnel itself may be white, brown or black in color.

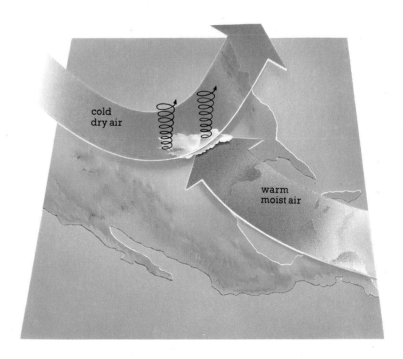

cold
dry air

warm
moist air

This map of the United States shows the collision of typical warm and cool air streams that causes tornadoes. The worst affected areas, in Kansas and Oklahoma, average up to 400 tornadoes each year.

The Spectacular Sky

The weather sometimes produces spectacular patterns of light and color in the sky. One of the most familiar is the great multicolored arc of a rainbow. Rainbows appear when the sun's light passes through raindrops. The sun sends out rays of light in a great variety of colors, but we cannot usually see them because when the rays are mixed together the light appears clear. However, the rays are bent, or refracted, as they enter and leave the raindrops. Because light from the sun is made up from many different wavelengths, some rays are refracted more than others, and so the light leaves the raindrop with the colors slightly separated. Rainbows usually appear to have seven colors: red – which is bent the least – orange, yellow, green, blue, indigo, and violet – which is bent the most. What we often do not see is the gradual change from one color to the next, beginning with the red band on the outside and ending with the violet band on the inside.

Sometimes a second, fainter rainbow can be seen outside the main one. This is due to the light being reflected twice inside the raindrops, first at one angle, then at another. Because of this double reflection the colors of the secondary rainbow are reversed, with the red on the inside and violet on the outside. The sky between the two bows looks darker than the rest of the sky because any other reflected light travels either inside the primary bow or outside the secondary bow.

In other weather conditions, a ring can often be seen surrounding the sun or moon. The largest rings, called halos, usually look white, but sometimes they

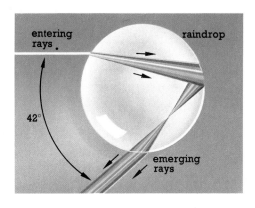

A rainbow forms when light entering raindrops is reflected and at the same time refracted, so that the light emerges split into its constituent colors. Because the angle between the entering and emerging rays is 42°, rainbows always have an arc of 42° radius.

The well-defined arcs of a double rainbow are seen here on a mountainside on Oahu in the Hawaiian Islands.

This brilliant winter sunset over Plymouth, England, produced part of a halo as the sun sank behind a thickening bank of clouds.

A layer of high, altocumulus clouds produced this luminous corona around the moon.

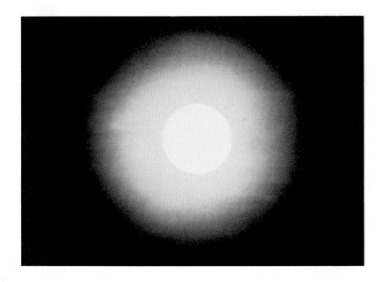

have several bands of color. They appear when a thin sheet of cirrostratus clouds, made of ice crystals, passes in front of the sun or moon, refracting and reflecting its rays. Halos are said to be a sign of rain and this is often true, because a sheet of cirrostratus clouds tends to develop and thicken as a low-pressure area approaches.

Halos should not be confused with coronas, which are smaller and occur when there is a layer of altocumulus clouds, made of water droplets. Coronas often have bands of color too, with the red band, which is diffused the most, on the outside. Although they occur around both the sun and moon, they are usually noticed only around the moon, because the sun is too dazzling to look at in such conditions. A corona is not a sign of rain because altocumulus clouds do not normally herald an approaching low.

Energy from the Weather

Most of the energy consumed by the industrialized nations comes from oil, coal, and gas. All of these fossil fuels are limited, and will sooner or later be entirely exhausted. However, we also have access to almost limitless energy in the form of sunshine, wind, and water power and these are gaining importance as our fossil fuel resources become increasingly scarce.

The sun is one of our most promising energy sources. Every year it bombards the earth's surface with energy equivalent to more than 90 thousand billion tons of coal. We can tap some of this vast power source by using solar panels. These are usually flat sheets of blackened metal, behind which water circulates in tubes. The dark surface absorbs the sun's heat and transfers it to the water, which can then be used for heating, bathing, or industrial processes. In some parts of the world there is enough sunshine for entire houses to be heated like this in winter. But since there are always days when the sun does not shine, another form of energy, such as oil or electricity, must be kept in reserve.

In the future, larger solar panels could be placed in a desert region, and if these covered a very large area – perhaps several square miles – they could generate as much electricity as a modern nuclear power station. Scientists have also suggested fitting satellites with solar collectors to transmit heat down to power stations on earth. Advances of this sort could mean that by the year 2000 a significant proportion of the world's energy supply may come directly from the sun.

The wind is another source of energy. It was once used to power windmills that could grind wheat to make flour. In The Netherlands windmills are still

This photograph shows the massive engineering involved in developing one of the world's largest rain-fed hydroelectric schemes, the Kariba Dam, in Zimbabwe.

used to prevent fields from flooding, by pumping water away. Nowadays new designs of windmills are being used to generate electricity. One of the largest of these modern windmills, at Tvind in Denmark, is over 165 feet high, with three blades each weighing five tons. When working at full power it provides enough electricity to light 120 homes.

To make building a windmill worthwhile, it must be located where there are plenty of days when the wind is strong. Unfortunately, not many parts of the world have this sort of weather – and those that do are often distant from the towns and cities that need electricity. One solution might be to construct groups of giant windmills high on windy hillsides.

There is also an enormous amount of energy in a waterfall or fast-flowing river. Hydroelectric power stations are built to take advantage of this energy, using the force of the falling water to turn turbines and generate electricity. Because on most rivers the strength of the flow normally varies from day to day

This windmill at Boone, North Carolina, is 140 feet tall and has a pair of blades 200 feet long from end to end. It began operation in July 1979.

engineers build dams to hold back surplus water, which can then be released to provide a steady supply of energy. Only a fraction of the world's potential for hydroelectric power is at present being used; up to three times as much power could be supplied by water in the United States, and up to nine times in the Soviet Union. However, developing this potential poses major environmental problems. Large dams can ruin the appearance of scenic upland areas, and may cause serious upstream flooding and silting.

These specially designed parabolic mirrors form part of an experimental solar collector at Sandia Laboratories in the sun-baked countryside of New Mexico.

Measuring the Weather

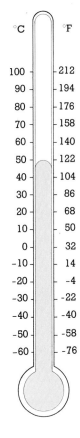

Before tomorrow's weather can be forecast today's weather has to be measured. Simply noting that the weather is cold, windy and wet is not enough. It is necessary to know precisely how cold, what the wind speed and direction are, and how much rain has fallen. Many different instruments are used to make these measurements.

Most people are familiar with thermometers, which are often marked with two sets of figures, the Fahrenheit scale and the Centigrade scale. To get an accurate air temperature, the thermometer must be in the shade. Most meteorologists take temperature readings from a thermometer shaded by a housing called a Stevenson Screen, after its inventor. As an additional check other types of thermometers are also used. For example, a strip can be formed of two metals which expand at different rates when heated. The resulting curl of the strip can then be directly correlated to temperature variations. Other thermometers make use of the fact that the electrical resistance of a metal wire varies according to the temperature.

Humidity is measured by two thermometers placed side by side, one of which – called a wet-bulb thermometer – has a small piece of wet gauze tied around its bulb. If the humidity is 100 per cent, the thermometers read the same; but if it is less, water evaporates from the cloth, lowering the temperature of the bulb. The greater the difference between the temperatures, the lower the humidity level.

Atmospheric pressure is measured with a barometer. The face of a barometer is usually marked off in units called millibars. Air pressure at the surface of the earth is normally between 960 and 1040 millibars. The higher the figure, the higher the pressure. The barometer is a useful register of daily pressure changes. After the pressure has been falling for a while the weather usually becomes more unsettled, with rain or snow, clouds, and wind. If air pressure

The barometer shown above contains a vacuum chamber which is connected by levers to the black pointer. As pressure rises or falls the chamber contracts or expands, moving the pointer. The bronze indicator, which can be set by hand, reflects the previous pressure readings. The double-scale thermometer on the right gives a convenient comparison of Fahrenheit (°F) and Centigrade (°C) measurements.

is rising, clear weather is probably on the way.

Wind speed is measured by an anemometer, of which there are several different types. The one used most often works rather like a toy windmill. Three cups are set on a spindle, and the stronger the wind the faster they spin around. The wind speed, in miles per hour, is shown on a dial, in the same way that a speedometer shows how fast a car is going. Wind direction is shown by a wind or weather vane, and also by a wind sock.

The second most common anemometer can also show wind direction. The instrument consists of a small propeller mounted on a shaft, like the fuselage of an aircraft without wings. The shaft is able to swivel to the direction of the wind, which powers the propeller.

Precipitation is measured with a rain or snow gauge, a simple device in which a funnel collects

rainwater and directs it into a bottle. Each day an observer empties the bottle into a measuring cylinder. The area of the cylinder is only a tenth of that of the top of the funnel, so that a tenth of an inch of rain will be one inch deep in the cylinder, making it easier to measure accurately. If snow falls in the gauge, the observer has to melt it before the amount of precipitation can be measured.

A total precipitation of one inch means that, if all the rainfall stayed on the ground where it fell, the ground would be covered with a layer of water one inch deep. In the temperate zone, a typical day's precipitation is 0.8 inches, while figures for a year in the same zone would be between 20 and 40 inches.

Hours of sunshine are commonly measured by either of two instruments. One is called a Campbell-Stokes recorder (see photograph at left). The other uses a device similar to a thermometer, in which sunshine heats a column of mercury. The expanding mercury rises and closes an electric switch, sending a pulse of energy along a wire to a recording device, which therefore provides meteorologists with a continuous record of sunshine.

This sunshine recorder (left) is widely used as an alternative to the sunshine switch. A glass sphere is used to concentrate sunlight which produces a charred line, corresponding to periods of sunshine, on a strip of paper.

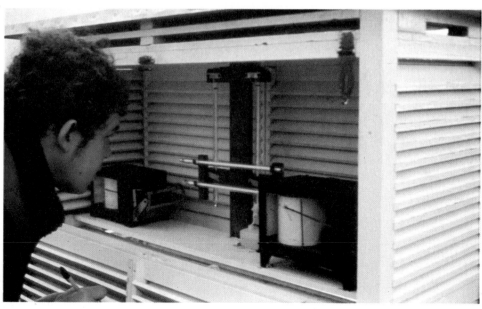

Observers take regular readings from the instruments in a Stevenson Screen, a standard meteorological housing for thermometers. The pair of vertical thermometers measure humidity, the horizontal ones maximum and minimum temperatures. Humidity and temperature are also recorded on charts by the hydrograph (right) and the thermograph (left) respectively.

Information Gathering

Weather systems are continually shifting and changing. To make accurate forecasts, meteorologists at about 10,000 weather stations in all parts of the world cooperate in making detailed observations regularly and at set times.

Every three hours, day and night, these meteorological observers read instruments and record the local humidity, wind direction, wind speed, temperature and barometric pressure. In addition, every six hours they note the maximum and minimum temperatures, and check their precipitation gauges. They then translate this information into an international code which can be transmitted by radio or teleprinter. This information is now entered directly into computers in most parts of the United States. Generally the coded messages are first received at local weather centers. Each local center collects about 30 messages, from various climatological substations in its area, and then transmits all these messages to a national center. The national center in turn selects a representative sample of these messages and transmits it to other countries. In this way, in a very short time any weather center can obtain information about the weather over a large part of the globe.

At each national weather center meteorologists – often with the aid of a computer – plot as many as 2000 selected observations on a map called a synoptic chart. This is done by translating the code into symbols that show the state of the weather in any particular area. The meteorologists then use the measurements of atmospheric pressure to draw isobars, which show where low-pressure areas and anticyclones are situated. The position of rain areas is estimated by assuming that rain is falling in the area between adjacent stations that have reported precipitation. This area is usually colored green on the map. Finally, the meteorologists draw in the fronts – boundaries between air masses, which are indicated by sharp contrasts in wind, temperature, or humidity. Much of this work is now done by computers.

At the three World Meteorological Centres – in Moscow, Washington, D.C., and Melbourne, Australia – maps are plotted and drawn for the whole globe. Machines at these centers can translate the map into radio signals, which can be picked up by any office with a suitable receiver and turned back into maps. These can give a meteorologist in Moscow a bird's-eye view of the weather over, say, the tropical South Pacific within about three hours of the original observations being made.

At some observing stations a hydrogen-filled balloon is sent up every 12 hours carrying an

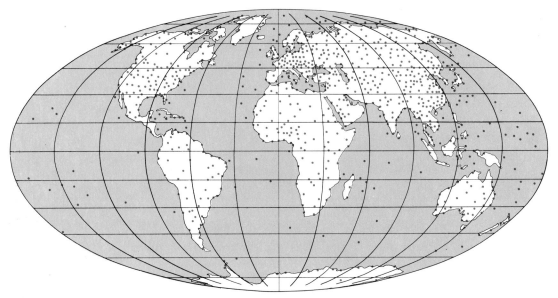

This map shows the extensive network of observing stations from which instrument-carrying radiosonde balloons are released. The information they provide is relayed to national and international meteorological centers.

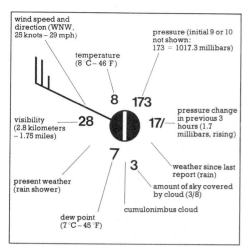

wind speed and direction (WNW, 25 knots – 29 mph)

temperature (8°C – 46°F)

pressure (initial 9 or 10 not shown: 173 = 1017.3 millibars)

visibility (2.8 kilometers – 1.75 miles)

pressure change in previous 3 hours (1.7 millibars, rising)

present weather (rain shower)

weather since last report (rain)

amount of sky covered by cloud (3/8)

cumulonimbus cloud

dew point (7°C – 45°F)

Coded reports, (above), appear on complex weather maps called synoptic charts that are compiled throughout the world.

The accuracy of synoptic charts depends on increasingly sophisticated observation. For example, the research balloon at right will carry instruments to a height of nearly 20 miles.

The British meteorologists in the photograph below are using facsimile transmission machines to send synoptic charts to Germany.

instrument called a radiosonde that measures the temperature, humidity, and pressure at different atmospheric levels, and transmits the information back to the ground by radio. The balloon rises to a maximum height of about 100,000 feet, then bursts, and the package of instruments returns safely to the ground by parachute. The wind speed and direction at different heights can be calculated in the office by using radio direction-finding equipment, which tracks the movement of the radiosonde as it drifts with the air currents. This information is used by meteorologists to draw charts showing the weather in the upper atmosphere, which has an important influence on the movement of weather systems at lower levels.

Satellites

Since the launching of Tiros I by the United States in April 1960, satellites have been providing meteorologists with a wealth of previously unobtainable information about the world's weather. Meteorological satellites carry two main types of equipment: normal light cameras for taking daytime photographs of cloud formations, and infrared cameras that can locate clouds at night by the heat they give off.

The cloud systems revealed by satellite photographs can easily be identified. Long bands of clouds indicate fronts; and large masses of clouds into which the fronts spiral are low-pressure areas. Speckled areas indicate cumulus or cumulonimbus clouds – probably producing showers.

In addition to cameras, some satellites carry an instrument called a radiometer, designed to sense the temperature of different layers of the atmosphere. This means that meteorologists can obtain records of atmospheric temperature at different levels at virtually any location on the earth's surface. Although high-level weather balloons can do the same job for a single place, a satellite can scan large areas of the earth's surface and take measurements over regions such as the South Atlantic, where there are only a few widely scattered weather stations.

The weather satellite ESSA 9 leaves the launch pad at Cape Kennedy in February 1969. Photographs of the earth from space have revolutionized our understanding of large-scale weather systems.

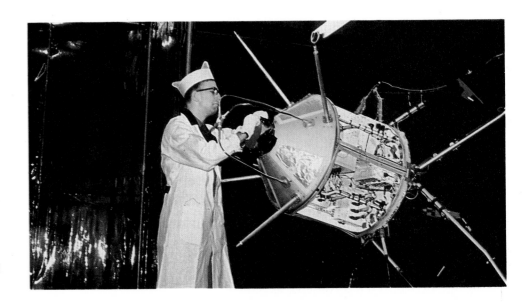

A technician makes final adjustments to the British weather satellite UK3 before its launch at an international test range.

A photograph taken by the NASA satellite ATS 3 of Mexico and part of the United States delineates large-scale cloud systems that would be impossible to plot accurately from the ground.

Weather satellites are placed in two kinds of orbit, polar and geosynchronous. Satellites on a polar orbit – used in the first launchings – circle the earth from pole to pole at an altitude of about 530 miles. Each circuit takes about 100 minutes. And as the earth rotates, the satellite provides one complete survey of the world's weather every 24 hours. However, in 1966 the United States succeeded in making a satellite orbit the earth in such a way as to stay in a fixed position 2200 miles above one particular point on the Equator. This so-called geosynchronous orbit opened up a new dimension in satellite photography, since it enabled meteorologists to trace the step by step development of cloud systems and to follow their path across the earth's surface.

Satellites have revealed many new things about the weather, particularly in tropical areas. Meteorologists used to know very little about these tropical systems and therefore found it difficult to forecast changes in the weather in the tropics. But now the situation has changed. Satellites have revealed cloud clusters – large areas of patchy clouds that remain for a day or two and bring heavy showers and gusty winds. They also show lines of cloud very much like fronts, that bring rain, and rings or spirals of clouds that often develop into hurricanes.

Forecasting

When weather forecasters at a national weather center begin to compile data for a forecast, their first step is to study the most recent synoptic chart. Although this chart will still be a mass of numbers and symbols representing measurements of such key factors as temperature, wind speed and direction, pressure and precipitation from hundreds of observation stations, an experienced meteorologists can instantly get a feel for the general state of the weather by examining this material.

The next step involves comparing the most recent chart with those prepared during the previous 24 hour period. This may involve examining perhaps half a dozen synoptic charts. By studying the charts in sequence, a trained forecaster is able to trace the growth and decline of the major weather systems affecting his country or even an entire hemisphere. The meteorologists can also spot new developments when they are first forming and observe changes in speed and direction as the established systems move across the continent.

Satellite photographs provide additional material for the forecaster. Since these photographs show what actually existed in a specific area at a particular time, they can be used to check or even supplement the charts. For example, a snowstorm may have been predicted for an area 200 miles wide and several hundred miles or more in length. Although snow probably will fall at one time or another throughout the entire region, the heaviest snowfall at a particular time is usually confined to a much smaller area – perhaps no more than 50 miles wide and less than 100 miles long. However, since the area of intense activity is governed by very local conditions – a slight drop in temperature or a sudden shift in wind speed or direction – a forecaster cannot always tell in advance where the heaviest snow will fall. Satellite pictures provide this necessary detail. A meteorologist can actually see the storm, and by comparing a series of satellite photographs – usually taken every 30 minutes – he can plot the path of heavy snowfall. If necessary, revised forecasts or even blizzard warnings can be issued.

A meteorologist draws isobars and fronts on a synoptic chart to provide an instantly recognizable picture of the state of the atmosphere.

Radar reports also help the meteorologist compile accurate precipitation reports. Because radar waves are reflected by any form of precipitation, and because the degree of reflection is related to the size of the raindrop, snowflake or hailstone, the radar screen provides a picture of the intensity of any precipitation as well as the location. The National Weather Service in the United States operates a radar network covering all of the states east of the Rocky Mountains. It uses the Federal Aviation Administration's radar network for reports on the mountain regions in the western half of the country. A network of radar stations currently covers Wales and most of England permitting up-to-the-minute precipitation reports. When this radar data is used in conjunction with cloud photographs, a forecaster is able to tell which clouds are causing the rain.

Armed with all of the information provided by the radar reports, satellite pictures, the sequence of synoptic charts, and computerized data from weather observation posts throughout the hemisphere, the meteorologist is finally ready to attempt a prediction. Certain weather events such as fog or the difference between a freezing rain and a snowstorm will always be hard to predict. A slight change in temperature –

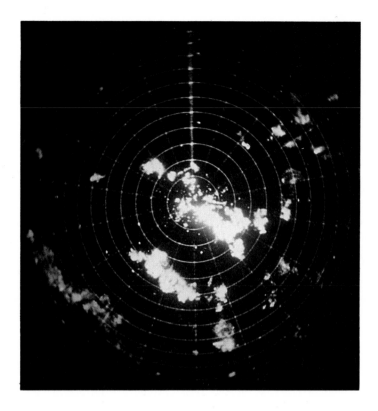

Satellite photographs provide vital information for the forecaster. This one shows Typhoon Bess off the southeast coast of Japan in September 1971.

A concentration of raindrops, indicating heavy showers, shows up as white blobs on a radar screen.

often no more than a degree or two – can turn a "slight chance of snow" into several inches. In the end, it is the chief meteorologist's interpretation of the data that results in specific predictions.

For anyone whose picnic has been spoiled by an unexpected shower, the science of forecasting seems to be little more than educated guessing. For a city sanitation engineer whose snow removal budget is prepared only after careful consultation with the meteorologist's office, the need for an accurate assessment is vital to a balanced budget. For cities close to rivers, rain forecasts and flood predictions may be a matter of life or death.

The United States Weather Service estimates that it makes about two million general weather forecasts each year. In addition to this, it issues special storm warnings and tornado bulletins, offers a regular flood forecast report and prepares nearly 750,000 aviation forecasts. In a recent study the service reported that one-day forecasts were correct more than 85 per cent of the time.

The Computer's Role in Forecasting

For centuries people have been attempting to formulate precise rules for predicting the future weather on the basis of the present. By using a variety of complex mathematical equations, scientists have been able to build up a numerical description of certain atmospheric conditions.

In the early 1950s, when computers were just becoming commercially available, meteorologists began using them to help describe the motion of air at a particular point in the atmosphere and under very specific conditions. Meteorologists explained that they were creating a hypothetical picture – or model – of what the atmosphere was like. Since even

the earliest computers were able to make hundreds of calculations in less time and with a greater degree of accuracy than individuals were able to do, meteorologists continued to use computers and computer-based models to learn as much as possible about the ways specific atmospheric conditions relate to specific kinds of weather. As computers have become more sophisticated in the last few decades, so have the atmospheric models meteorologists are able to construct.

Today the best computers can represent conditions of the atmosphere at 15 different levels for more than 2000 different points around the world. By having

A computer-produced forecast of pressure systems dated June 1, 1978, for the southern hemisphere.

A chart of the actual pressure systems on June 1, 1978, closely resembles the computer's predictions.

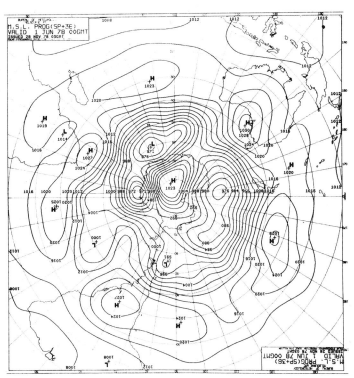

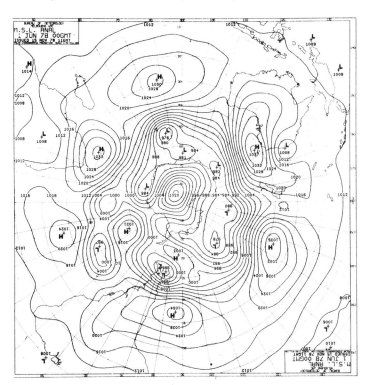

this much data instantly available, accurate relationships between air temperature and wind speed and direction can be used to predict the state of the atmosphere. At the British Meteorological Office in Bracknell, the computer repeats this process more than 100 times to come up with the next day's forecast.

The computer is also involved in basic weather research. Complex weather data is assembled by researchers and then programmed into the computer. Then specific conditions can be slightly altered – the wind speed increased by a few miles per hour or the air temperature lowered a degree. The effect of this slight change on the movement of an entire weather system can be examined in detail. Scientists in the United States are using computers in this way to help them understand the movement of hurricanes.

Meteorologists are equally interested in tornadoes, an especially violent and often destructive storm about which amazingly little is known. These storms, quite common in the United States, can be simulated in the laboratory by dropping salt crystals into a rotating beaker of soda water. Carbon dioxide from the soda forms bubbles around the salt crystals which, because the water is spinning, rise in an increasingly intense vortex. Calculations pertaining to the relationship between the spin and the rising bubbles can be programmed into computers and the results compared to actual tornado observations. In time this research may enable meteorologists to predict with a reasonable degree of accuracy the general area where a tornado might strike.

Computer forecasts are printed out on chart-plotting machines such as the one shown above left. Here, a tracing device moves back and forth across the chart, which is fixed to a sheet that moves up and down on rollers.

The computer at left, installed at the British Meteorological Office in 1981, can handle ten million pieces of information in one second. It is used for climate simulations as well as for short-term weather forecasts.

Advances in Meteorology

After World War Two the meteorological offices of more than 120 countries joined together to form the World Meteorological Organization, or WMO, which is now an agency of the United Nations. In 1968 the WMO began a long-term project known as the World Weather Watch, which involves the collecting of observations from 9000 meteoroligical stations, 700 upper-air weather balloon stations and 6000 merchant ships all over the globe. As part of the World Weather Watch a special project took place from 1974 to 1979. The project was known as the Global Atmospheric

Research ships off the coast of West Africa formed the grid shown below to monitor tropical cloud clusters in the Global Atmospheric Research Program of 1974. In the photograph below right, a technician checks meteorological instruments on a buoy, near one of the GARP research ships with its tethered weather blimp. Such facilities helped provide a complete picture of weather in the lower atmosphere.

Research Program, or GARP for short. Its purpose was to increase the accuracy of weather forecasts made for several days ahead by collecting a large number of extremely detailed observations. Because the project was far too expensive and complicated for any single country to carry out, many governments contributed equipment and funds. As a result GARP has been one of the world's most successful experiments in international cooperation.

One of the most interesting parts of GARP was a giant scientific experiment that took place during 100 days in 1974. Its object was to find out more about the behavior of the atmosphere in the tropics. There the heat and humidity make the atmosphere highly unstable. Warm humid air rises in powerful convection currents to as high as 40,000 feet and then travels up to 2000 miles north or south, affecting the weather over a vast area.

From June to September 1974, about 4000 scientists from 57 countries, together with 40 ships and 12 aircraft, gathered at the port of Dakar in tropical West

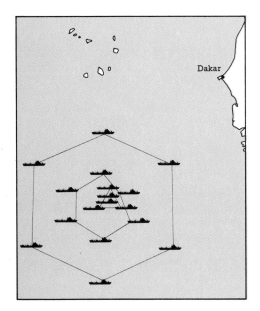

Africa. Then the ships were arranged in a network of positions over an area of 500 miles wide in the central Atlantic. Within this network they succeeded in monitoring the growth of a succession of cloud clusters – the visible sign of a strong convection current. Airplanes flew among the thunderclouds taking measurements of factors such as temperature, pressure and humidity, while satellites – particularly the GOES satellite, newly launched by the United States – provided meteorologists with detailed pictures of the cloud patterns. The detailed observations were relayed to computers, including nine extremely powerful systems in Japan, Britain, Canada and the United States.

The GARP project provided a unique opportunity to study in detail the behavior of the tropical atmosphere.

Even though it will be many years before all the observations are fully analyzed, scientists have already learned a great deal about convection in the tropics. They have discovered cloud systems that lie at right angles to the wind, like fronts, and others that stretch out along the wind. The detailed measurements made during the GARP experiment have helped tell how these cloud systems work, by showing where the air is rising and where it is sinking, where it is unstable, and where it is not. This knowledge is already helping meteorologists to make more accurate forecasts.

Advanced equipment is now used to obtain the maximum amount of information from satellite pictures. The television screen shows an image of clouds off northwest France relayed from the satellite Meteostat 2. This picture has been processed by computer to show dark clouds, and land surfaces, in green and red, light clouds in dark blue and light blue.

The British weather plane shown here has been specially adapted to take measurements in the upper atmosphere. The extended nose section places instruments in air that is not yet disturbed by the plane's passage.

Who Uses Forecasts?

Most of us are familiar with the weather forecasts that appear each day in newspapers or are broadcast on the radio or television. People often use them when deciding what to do – whether to go to the beach or to the movies, whether to take an umbrella or sunglasses. Yet weather forecasts have a much more important role: they are vital for some people's work and for the smooth running of many services that everyone takes for granted. Aircraft pilots need regular reports on the weather conditions along their route – particularly for takeoff or landing. Fog at airports is a serious hazard, and planes may have to be rerouted to avoid it. Major airports employ specially trained observers who take hourly readings of factors such as visibility, and wind direction and speed, and pass the information to pilots by radio. From many smaller airports across the United States pilots must telephone the nearest Flight Service Center for information of this kind.

Weather forecasts are indispensible to people putting out to sea in small boats, especially ones that depend on the wind for their power. Even the most experienced sailor wants to avoid being out at sea during a flat calm or a gale. Large ships are less affected by severe weather, but the wind does affect their speed. For example, wind from the stern of a ship can increase its speed by about one per cent while headwinds will decrease it by 3 to 13 per cent. Meteorological offices work out the best route for a ship to cross the ocean to take full advantage of the winds, and shipping companies can save up to ten per cent on the fuel bill of a transatlantic cargo liner by following the forecaster's advice.

The amount of electricity people use depends to a great extent on the weather. When the temperature drops they may turn up the heating, while in summer a rise in temperature makes air conditioners work harder, using more electricity. Unlike other forms of power, electricity cannot be stored for emergencies, and power stations need to know in advance when temperatures are going to change so that they can switch on extra generators. Otherwise the sudden demand may overload the capacity of the generating system, and cause a blackout.

American city dwellers use an average of 70

Commercial airliners such as this British Airways Trident can be paralyzed by fog, but with accurate forecasting a nation's air traffic can be diverted to unaffected airports.

A sea-rescue vessel battles through waves which have been whipped up by gale-force winds. Weather forecasts play a vital role in reducing the number of disasters at sea.

gallons of water every day. Therefore it is vital to manage supplies as efficiently as possible. Water authorities need to know if precipitation is forecast. If heavy or prolonged precipitation is expected, they will allow surplus water to overflow from reservoirs. If only light precipitation is likely they will store every drop they can collect. But if the rain is very heavy they may give warnings of floods. Water authorities use rain or snow gauges scattered over their area to collect information about rainfall. Some even use radar to tell where it is raining at any particular moment. This information helps to make quite accurate predictions of the total amount of water that will eventually find its way into reservoirs.

Farmers need weather forecasts almost all year around. They want to try to avoid sowing their seeds in a dry spell, because they will die before sending out any shoots, but on the other hand, they need dry weather for harvesting. Humid weather can bring diseases to plants, requiring the use of expensive chemical sprays, while if the weather stays dry crops need irrigation. In areas like Florida and Italy, fruit trees need to be protected from frosts which sometimes occur unexpectedly in late spring. Forecasts can warn of imminent frosts and may be extremely useful to farmers but cannot, of course, tell them exactly when to plant their crops.

A patrolman directs traffic in a New York street during a blizzard. Motorists often pay a heavy penalty for ignoring warnings of blizzards, some finding they have to abandon their vehicles.

The timing of the wheat harvest, seen here near Dutton, Montana, is often heavily dependent on correct weather forecasting. Accurate weather forecasting, if available on a regular basis, could enable farmers to avoid late frosts and to take advantage of timely rainfall.

Weather Lore

People have been making weather forecasts for thousands of years. Our ancestors watched for signs in the sky, or in the behavior of animals. Many people still use these ancient indicators, claiming that they are more reliable than the official forecasts. Modern research has shown that some of the notions are indeed quite useful, but others are nonsense.

"Red sky at night, sailor's delight
Red sky in the morning, sailor's warning."

This saying, which often substitutes the word shepherd for sailor, means that if the sky is red at sunset, the next day will probably be clear, but if the sky is red in the morning, rain is likely by nightfall. There is some truth in this rule. The sky is red when the sun is shining near the horizon and there are clouds higher up in the sky. In temperate latitudes, clouds usually move from west to east in both hemispheres, so if the sky is red at night, the clouds must be moving away. On the other hand, if the sky is red in the morning the cloud will just have arrived.

"Rain before seven, clear before eleven."

This rule of four hours to clearing weather works if weather systems are moving quickly, but there is nothing significant about the time of day. The rule would be just as true if it said "Rain before one, clear before five" – but that doesn't rhyme. All the rule really says is that rain may last for four hours. This is often true if the rain is caused by a low passing to the north, but it is not true if you are on the side of a low nearest the Pole, on a coast exposed to rain-bearing winds, or in the mountains.

"Long notice, long last,
Short notice, soon past."

This is a good general rule. Sometimes a spell of rain gives a day or two's warning that it is coming, with a gradual increase of cloudiness, a strengthening of the wind, and a slow fall of the barometer. The rainy spell will then probably last a few days. On other occasions, bad weather may come on very suddenly. If it does, the skies will probably clear just as quickly. The same applies to good weather. A bright, sunny day after a wet spell probably will last only a short time. But if the pressure rises slowly and the weather gradually gets warmer, the fine spell will last a few days or so.

Animals are held to be good weather forecasters. For example, cows are said to lie down before a summer storm and rabbits are supposed to sit looking in one direction with their ears twitching before a thunderstorm. It is even claimed that donkeys bray loudly and cats wash themselves thoroughly when it is going to rain. Some of these sayings may be true. But if they are, it is not because the animals are able to predict the weather. It simply means that they are more sensitive to changes of humidity or air pressure than humans are.

Although meteorologists are still unable to give reliable forecasts for more than a month ahead, there is plenty of folklore that claims to be able to do just this. Here are two examples:

"If the groundhog sees his shadow on
February 2, there will be six more
weeks of winter."

and, forecasting summer weather

"St Swithin's Day if thou dost rain
For forty days it will remain.
St Swithin's Day if thou be fair
For forty days 'twill rain nae mair."

The groundhog rule comes from the United States, while the rule referring to St Swithin's Day, July 15, originated in Britain. Taken literally the British rule obviously has little truth, because most places in Britain have never had 40 days of rain in a row at any time of the year, let alone after July 15. There are sayings in many European countries, all stating nearly the same thing. For example, there is a similar rule for February 2, Candlemas Day:

"If Candlemas Day be fair and bright
Winter will have another fight.
If Candlemas Day brings clouds and rain
Winter is gone and won't come again."

Although no particular day can ever enable us to predict with any real accuracy what the next month's weather will be, there has been just enough intermittent sense in these rules to maintain their popularity over scores and even hundreds of years.

This groundhog's shadow shows accurately that the day is sunny. But it is unlikely to predict correctly another six weeks of winter, as the old folktales claim.

Red sky at night brings the promise of a fine day to come.

These cows make doubtful prophets as they lie down in hot sunny weather when, traditionally, they are said to lie down before a storm.

Living with the Weather

Houses in Sumatra, Indonesia, are built on stilts for protection against flooding. The stream, in which the man is standing, will become a swollen river when the monsoon arrives.

Igloos use snow as an insulator – a brilliant way of turning the results of extreme weather to man's advantage. A ledge runs along the interior wall, enabling the occupants to sit in the zone of warmer air near the "roof."

For as long as human beings have lived in shelters they have adapted them to the particular climate in which they lived. Although modern buildings tend to look the same wherever they are built, traditional architecture still shows wide differences according to climate, with building materials, doors, windows, and overall shapes of the dwellings all dictated by a particular mixture of weather.

In cool, temperate climates, houses tend to be solidly built, with thick walls for insulation and big windows on the sunny side to let in as much of the sun's warmth as possible. In hot climates, however, where there is a great deal of sunshine, houses are designed to provide shade, and to let the maximum amount of air circulate through the interior. For example, older houses in the southeastern United States have wide overhanging roofs, verandahs, and an open interior with few dividing walls or doors.

In desert regions, where scorching afternoon sunshine is often followed by a rapid drop in temperature at night, houses need to have thick walls. The walls provide insulation that helps to balance out temperature differences, so that rooms are cooler than the outside by day, and warmer by night.

Thick walls are just as important in cold, windy places. There, they help to keep heat in – rather than out. If made of a heavy material, they also help to keep the building firmly anchored to the ground in strong winds. Low-pitched roofs provide additional wind protection. A lightweight tropical house with its characteristic steeply pitched roof for deflecting heavy rain, would not only be unbearably cold to live in if it were built in, say, Scotland or eastern Canada: it would probably blow away within a few months.

In modern times it has become possible to heat or cool virtually any building as much as we like with central heating or air conditioning. Because of this, houses, offices, and factories can now be built to the same design in widely differing climates, and tall

Without double glazing or blinds, the glass walls of skyscrapers let in the sun's heat in summer, and allow huge quantities of heat to escape in cold winter weather.

This house in Pakistan has windcatchers on its roof, to divert cool breezes into the interior and provide a simple but efficient form of air conditioning.

office blocks with wide expanses of glass, are a familiar feature of modern cities the world over. However, there is no real advantage in making buildings so similar, and to do so can waste a lot of energy. For example, in the United States about 30 per cent of all the energy consumed is used for heating and cooling houses and offices. By constructing buildings to take maximum advantage of climate, this figure could be reduced to as little as 15 per cent.

A well-designed modern building in Minnesota or Maine should have large windows facing south to capture the near-horizontal rays of winter sunshine. However, glass is a very poor conductor of heat and windows in cold climates should always be constructed of two layers of glass with a pocket of air – which is a very good insulator – sandwiched in between them. By contrast, a modern house in southern

California should follow traditional Spanish designs, which avoid large areas of glass in favor of well-shaded window openings for ventilation.

Large concentrations of closely spaced buildings can sometimes affect the weather. For example, on a clear night the air in the center of a large city may be up to 7°F warmer than in the surrounding countryside, producing what is called a "heat island" effect. There are several reasons for this. A great deal of artificial heat is produced to keep our houses and offices warm and to power our factories. Also, on a warm day brick and concrete absorb heat and then give it out slowly at night. This has its advantages; for example, snowfall will settle less and melt more quickly in modern cities. Finally, large modern buildings tend to block the wind, which would otherwise tend to disperse pockets of warmer air.

Weather and Our Bodies

A tribesman in West Africa protects his face and body by thick clothing against scorching sunshine and desert dust storms.

This climber, 20,000 feet up in the Himalayas, is protected against extreme cold by the parka, trousers and boots he wears.

Our normal body temperature of 98.6°F is the result of heat generated by the many chemical processes that keep the body functioning. We can usually get rid of surplus heat through perspiration. This covers our skin with a thin film of water, which has a cooling effect as it evaporates. But in very hot conditions, this mechanism may prove inadequate. Then if our internal organs become warmer than 106°F, a strain is placed on the heart which may cause irreversible brain damage, because of reduced blood flow over several hours. However, individuals have survived internal temperatures of 112°F.

Spells of unusually hot weather can cause a noticeable increase in the mortality rate. For example, in Illinois during 1966, the hottest July for ten years brought a 36 per cent increase in deaths, mainly from heatstroke. In addition a hot sunny climate brings a greater risk of skin cancer because the body cells are very susceptible to ultraviolet radiation, which reaches high levels in strong sunshine. White skinned people living in the tropics – for example, white settlers in northern Australia – are particularly prone to skin cancer. Black skins on the other hand, possess a protection in the form of large amounts of the skin pigment melanin, which acts as a barrier against many of the effects of ultraviolet radiation.

If the air temperature falls below about 86°F, an unclothed body in a state of rest will start shivering to keep warm. Shivering, which generates heat from the processes involved in muscular movement, is a vital part of the body's survival mechanism. If our skin temperature falls to 50°F the sensations of pain and touch are lost, while if our internal temperature falls below about 90°F coma occurs. A temperature of 78.8°F or less may well cause death.

Wind strength can greatly affect how cold we feel. The stronger the wind the colder the air seems because the wind blows away the layer of warm air that usually lies next to our skin. If the temperature is 30°F and the wind speed 20 miles per hour, we feel as cold as if the temperature were 10°F on a windless day. This is known as the wind-chill factor.

Relative humidity has an important influence on our general well-being. At 70°F the most comfortable level of humidity is about 60 per cent. With higher levels the air feels increasingly sticky and we tend to tire more easily, while at lower levels, say, below 35 per cent, we may begin to suffer from a dry throat.

Different sorts of weather can increase our susceptibility to certain diseases. Colds seem to be more frequent when a cold spell is followed by a sudden warming. Influenza outbreaks are more common when relative humidity is below 50 per cent with only light winds. In both cases it seems that the weather conditions favor the growth and development of the viruses that cause the disease.

Our mental health also seems to be affected by weather. People have long suspected a connection between warm, dry, strong winds – such as the so-called Foehn wind of south-central Europe – and mental stress. Tempers also appear to rise in extremely hot weather. This seems to be borne out by various studies in southern California, which have revealed an apparent rise in the homicide rate when the blistering Santa Ana blows for a sustained period of time.

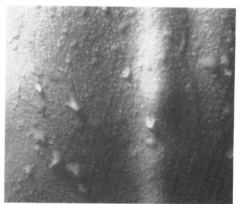

Perspiration, shown here in a close-up of a small portion of a person's bare back, is the body's own air conditioner. As perspiration evaporates, it creates a cool micro-climate on the surface of the skin.

Sunbathers enjoy subtropical sunshine on a Florida beach. When air temperatures are in the mid-80s Fahrenheit, as here, a lightly clothed body has no tendency to either perspire or shiver.

Climate and Crops

Weather, and especially temperature, is the single most important influence on the growth of crops. Plants grow more slowly at lower temperatures, and fruits stop growing altogether when the temperature falls below 40°F. Some grains can continue to grow at 32°F. This means that most parts of the world have a warm growing season and a cold dormant season.

Many fruits, such as oranges, peaches, and apricots, require a warm climate with plenty of sunshine and no frost. They grow well in areas such as California, Florida, the Mediterranean countries, and southern Australia, but unfortunately these places do get occasional frosts, which can ruin crops. Apples and plums, which grow well in northern areas, can survive frost as long as it does not occur while the trees are in blossom. However, frost can be a major hazard to coffee plantations. In July 1975 a cold snap of 21°F affected an estimated 70 per cent of coffee trees in southern Brazil, reducing the year's coffee production by almost 20 per cent.

Rainfall, of course, is vital to plants. Nearly all crops need a regular water supply, and some, such as rice, need to grow in pools of water. Wheat, on the other hand, prefers drier climates but still needs some rainfall throughout the growing season. Corn needs plentiful water during its growing season.

Even in very dry regions many crops will still grow if they are irrigated – usually by spraying with water that has been piped from a river or pumped up from underground. Parts of California have hardly any rain in summer, but fruits such as apricots, lemons, and peaches can be grown there because they are

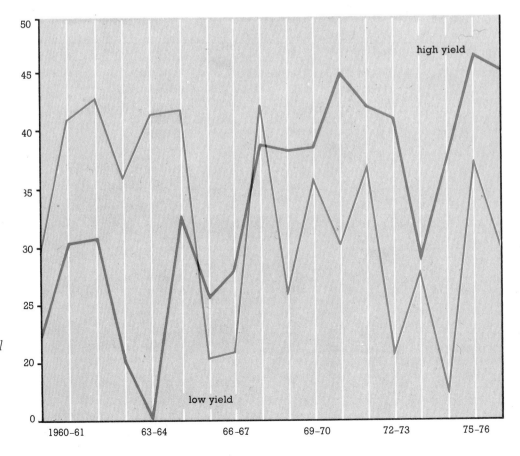

This graph shows the generally close correlation between wheat yield (red line) and summer rainfall (blue line) in Uttar Pradesh, India, from 1959 to 1977. Crop failure in 1963–4 was due to a winter cold spell followed by a delay in the onset of spring rains.

Blight on this American corn is the damaging result of an unusually damp summer.

This picture shows rice paddies in Szechuan, China, where the cultivation of rice is heavily dependent on the annual monsoon rains.

irrigated with water stored in reservoirs in the mountains. In places that usually get enough rain, irrigation is still a great help to the farmer in years when the summer is drier than average.

There is an ideal climate for every crop, so farmers must carefully consider their local climate before choosing which crops to grow. In India, for example, where the monsoon rains are heavy and the weather is warm, rice grows well. In the United States, corn thrives in states such as Illinois and Indiana which normally have warm, rainy summers. In the western prairies of both the United States and Canada the climate is too dry for corn but ideal for spring wheat.

The climate in southern Britain favors wheat and barley, but in the more northerly parts of temperate latitudes – for example Scotland – oats are the main crop because they take less time to grow than wheat and are more suited to wet springs and cool summers. In western Britain the climate is too wet for grain, but sheep and cattle thrive on the lush grass.

Scientists are now creating varieties of crops that are tailor-made to suit a particular climate. For example, plant breeders are creating drought-resistant strains of potato and varieties of sugar beet and barley able to tolerate frosts. However, the new strain may be more susceptible to sudden changes in climate, or unusually cold or wet weather, than traditional strains.

Crops may suffer from diseases, and some of these are encouraged by particular sorts of weather. For example, a cool, rainy period can encourage blight on potatoes and scab on apples. Farmers can protect the plants against these diseases by spraying, but this is expensive (certain sprays are also illegal in some countries) and it must be done before the disease develops. Fortunately many diseases depend on weather before the growing season, so farmers can decide whether an outbreak is likely. Leaf rust on wheat, for example, depends on temperature and humidity in late winter and early spring.

The Last Thousand Years

In Europe and parts of North America people have been measuring temperature and precipitation continuously for nearly three hundred years. We therefore have a great deal of information about how the climate has changed during that time. Before the year 1700, however, very few daily records were kept – although there are many references to weather in old documents and journals. However, climatologists have developed ways of tracing back the world's weather for many hundreds of years.

One of the most reliable ways of finding out about past climates is carried out by dendrochronologists, who measure the thickness of tree rings. When a tree is cut down, a pattern of concentric rings can be seen extending outward from the center of the trunk. A new ring forms each year, so each ring is made up of the wood that grew in one season. If a given year had moist, warm weather that encouraged growth, the ring for that year would be wide, while a year of poor growing weather would produce a narrow ring. By counting back from the present day, climatologists can work out the exact year that each ring represents. If they then measure relative widths of the rings, they can establish yearly variations in precipitation. And if they then analyze tree rings in different parts of the region, they can produce an

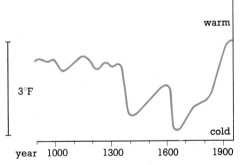

This graph of average temperatures in eastern Europe over the past thousand years reveals the cooling that occurred between the fourteenth and nineteenth centuries.

Close scrutiny of tree rings, such as the ones revealed in this damaged bristlecone pine, are examined at laboratories to provide a unique record of past climatic changes.

84

approximate map of precipitation over the country for a particular period hundreds of years ago. However, tree-ring research is rarely as straightforward as this. For example, toward the Equator a thin ring probably signifies a dry summer, whereas in more northerly areas it may mean a cool winter.

Other valuable clues come from botanists who, by analyzing samples of soils laid down in previous centuries, can discover seeds and pollen which reveal the type of vegetation that once grew in a given area. Since the growth of a particular species of plant often depends on a very narrow range of temperature and rainfall this type of research can give climatologists insight into the climate of the past.

Researchers have now pieced together a picture – vague in some places but remarkably clear in others – of how the climate has changed over the past thousand years. In the period 900 to 1300 AD the northern hemisphere was warmer than it is now. Many parts of England had flourishing vineyards. Iceland had a thriving civilization, and grain was grown there. In Greenland the temperature was between 2°F and 7°F warmer than it is now, and the Vikings were able to set up colonies in places where the ground is now frozen solid all year around. The Vikings also sailed across the far north of the Atlantic to North America, using a route that is now very risky in small boats because of frequent storms and the hazard of icebergs.

During the next few centuries the climate became

In February 1814 the Thames in London was sufficiently frozen to allow this fair to take place on the ice. By comparison with this season in the Little Ice Age, winters in the past century have been mild.

colder and often wetter. The coldest period, 1450 to 1850, has been called the Little Ice Age. By carefully analyzing rock and soil deposits, geologists and botanists have discovered that glaciers in the mountains of Europe and North America extended farther than they had for thousands of years. In northern countries, such as Scotland, crop failures were frequent: a cold spell of six years, when the harvest did not ripen and people were threatened with starvation, was probably one of the main reasons why Scotland united with England in 1707.

In North America tree-ring dating has shown that a great drought occurred at the end of the thirteenth century. Arizona in particular became much drier, and archaeological evidence reveals that some Indian tribes abandoned their villages and moved to wetter areas.

From about 1850 the climate gradually became warmer over most of the northern hemisphere. Between 1919 and 1939, for example, England had only one severe winter, but since 1940 the climate has become cooler, with several cold winters. Further north, Arctic ice reached the northeast coast of Iceland in 1968 for the first time in 40 years.

Glaciers

Large masses of ice called glaciers cover places near the Poles, such as Greenland and Spitsbergen, Norway. The biggest glacier in the world covers most of the Antarctic continent – in places to a depth of 10,000 feet – and contains such a massive volume of frozen water that if it melted, the level of the seas and oceans over the whole globe would rise by about 230 feet.

All glacial ice starts off as snow. When snow first falls it settles lightly on the ground. But as it continues falling, it builds into a thick layer. The delicate points of the snow crystals break off, so that the crystals form a more compact mass. In addition, the snow at the bottom becomes compressed. The increase in pressure results in an increase in temperature, so each crystal melts briefly and releases any air trapped inside. The water produced then freezes again, this time into a solid mass of ice.

Glaciers come into being in areas that are never warm enough for all the snow that falls in winter to melt in summer. The result is a buildup of snow year after year, and this gradually turns into thick layers of ice. Areas in which glaciers occur include not only the north and south polar regions but many of the world's high mountain ranges such as the Alps, the Andes, and the Himalayas. Even very high mountains near the Equator have glaciers on their tops: Mount Kilimanjaro in Tanzania, only 210 miles south of the Equator, has several small glaciers on its peak.

Climatologists study glaciers by drilling holes in them and drawing out long cores of ice, in which they can see distinct layers. The thickness of each layer indicates how much snow fell in a particular winter. Thus glacial ice, like tree rings, can provide

This photograph shows the glaciated interior of the Antarctic, the world's coldest continent. Though barely protruding above the ice-cap, these mountains are in fact thousands of feet high.

The Saskatchewan Glacier in the Rocky Mountains, Canada is typical of mountain ice-flows. It flows downhill a few hundred yards in a year.

climatologists with a detailed record of past climatic change. Even when individual layers of ice cannot be distinguished, the thickness of the glaciers will be a good guide to its age.

Although glaciers appear solid, they can travel down slopes by gradually deforming through a very slow process known as plastic flow. As a glacier travels, its tremendous weight gouges out a deep U-shaped valley which looks very different from a V-shaped valley carved by a river. Many mountainous, but ice-free, areas have such U-shaped valleys, which suggests that there must have been a period in the past when these areas were buried under ice.

The U-shaped valley of Llanberis in Wales is unmistakable evidence of the gouging action of a now vanished glacier.

Ice Ages

Although glacial ice cores give us an invaluable record of past climates, the layers of ice taken from great depths have become compressed together and so are difficult to distinguish from one another. So the age of the lowest layers must be worked out in another way.

The oxygen in water – and therefore in ice – is slightly radioactive, and its radioactivity decreases at a known rate for each year. This enables scientists to calculate the age of ice at a particular depth by measuring the radioactivity in that part of the core. Researchers using this technique, known as the isotope method, have analyzed ice cores taken from thousands of feet beneath the Greenland ice sheet and built up a picture of how the climate behaved over the millenia. The details of this story are still in doubt, but one thing is certain – the climate used to be much colder than it is now.

About 1.75 million years ago began the most recent of the earth's ice ages – spans of time during which cold glacial periods alternated with warm spells. As the climate became gradually colder, ice started to build up. There were some fluctuations as temperatures rose for a few thousand years, then went down again. But by about 15,000 to 20,000 years ago

This Danish researcher holds a core of Greenland ice, taken from a depth of more than one and a half miles. One segment such as this can reveal climatic fluctuations for almost 100,000 years.

The graph below shows world temperatures over the past 900,000 years, registered by changes in global ice volume. The graph below right shows winter severity in Europe over the past 20,000 years.

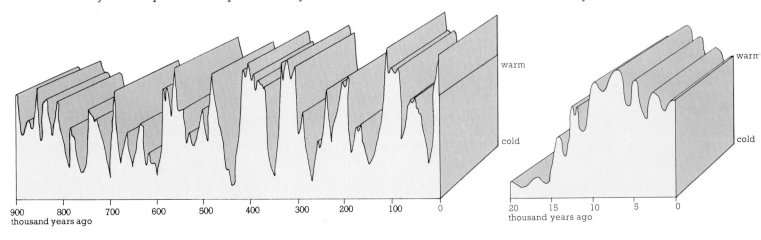

average temperatures all over the globe were approximately 10°F to 15°F lower than they are now. Ice covered Canada and the United States as far south as New York, and Europe as far south as London and Cologne. Mountain glaciers were much bigger than they are now, and many mountains in the tropical zone, such as Mauna Kea in Hawaii, had glaciers on their summits. Worldwide changes also occurred in the oceans, which were partly emptied due to the large amount of water distributed over land areas as ice. The drop in sea level was so great that dry land connected Asia and North America, Britain and Europe, and Australia and New Guinea.

Temperatures then began to rise again. The warming occurred relatively quickly – it took about 12,000 years to reach the warmest time. But for the past 6000 years the earth has been slowly cooling again, with fluctuations lasting anything from a few hundred to 2000 years. The so-called Little Ice Age (actually a brief glacial period) of 1450 to 1850 was the coldest period since the last major cold spell. By comparison, however, the temperature fluctuation in this recent cold period was very minor.

Over the past 900,000 years, there have been about ten major cold periods – scientists are not certain of the exact number – each separated by a warm period lasting about 10,000 years. Going back still further three major ice ages can be traced during the previous 600 million years. But it seems that for most of the earth's history there has probably been no permanent ice anywhere. This means that, relatively speaking, we are in the grip of an ice age now.

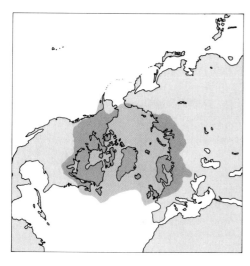

This map shows the northern hemisphere at the height of the last glacial period, with the polar ice-cap stretching as far south as southern Russia and the central United States.

A low Arctic sun highlights this remote research station in northern Greenland where drilling teams work through the brief summer to unravel the complex history of the earth's climate.

Are We Changing the Climate?

Some climatologists believe that the world's climates are gradually getting colder and that we will eventually find ourselves in the grip of another severe glacial period. This would devastate many of the world's major grain growing regions and so have a catastrophic effect on food supplies.

Any attempts at artificially warming the climate (notions as far-fetched as scattering black soot over the Arctic ice-caps have been proposed) would probably do more harm than good. Atmospheric circulations might change, bringing droughts to

This map shows the catastrophe that would be caused in Europe by a change in sea level resulting from the melting of both polar ice-caps. Labels indicate capital cities which would be submerged.

wheat growing areas and reducing the world's food supply. In addition, the warmer climate could start melting the thick continental ice over Greenland and the Antarctic. This would raise the sea level all over the world, and slowly drown low-lying cities such as New York, Bombay, London, and Sydney.

On the other hand, we may be altering the climate by accident. During the past century the industrialized nations have been burning more and more fuel, especially coal, oil, and gas, and this has released large amounts of carbon dioxide into the atmosphere. We have also been cutting down forests, and covering large areas of the land with roads and buildings. This has reduced the area covered by plants, which absorb carbon dioxide from the atmosphere as part of the process of photosynthesis. As a result, the proportion of carbon dioxide in the air is increasing.

Carbon dioxide acts rather like the glass walls of a greenhouse. It allows all the sun's rays to pass through to the earth's surface, but absorbs some of the heat that the earth radiates out and sends it back to the ground. Thus, the more carbon dioxide there is in the air, the warmer the earth will become. However, there is still a great deal of uncertainty as to the precise workings of climatic change. The short-term increase in temperature produced by high concentrations of carbon dioxide may cause an increase in cloudiness, giving more precipitation in the form of snow in polar regions and leading to an enlargement of the ice area.

The other effects of modern industry on the atmosphere may be just as severe. Factories are continually unloading dust and smoke into the air, which intercept some of the sun's heat before it can reach the ground, and radiate it back out to space, making the earth colder. The contrails, or vapor trails, made by jet airplanes have a similar effect. They are simply man-made clouds and, like them, reflect away some of the sun's heat. One contrail has hardly any effect on the climate, but we now produce many thousands every day, and they might have an important effect on the delicate balance between heat gained and heat lost.

Some meteorologists believe that exhaust gases from supersonic aircraft may damage the ozone layer of the stratosphere. Ozone results from the interaction of oxygen and ultraviolet radiation and once formed acts as a shield that protects us against the burning effects of this radiation. The gradual destruction of ozone could therefore have serious effects on earth's animal and plant life.

Steam from a British power station forms a vast artificial cloud that intercepts the sun's rays. Large-scale industrial activity threatens the delicate balance of the earth's climates.

The Future of Forecasting

Today meteorologists, with their sophisticated computer systems, are able to make reasonably accurate forecasts for as much as five days in advance. If sufficiently detailed information for the entire world could be gathered and then processed, a fairly accurate two-week forecast might be possible. Beyond that period, however, most meteorologists are not willing to speculate.

Even the forecast for tomorrow contains a good measure of educated guessing by the most experienced weathermen. As one research meteorologist explained it, to remove the guessing from the science of weather forecasting would require a frequent weather report for every two square inches of the earth's surface. This need for tremendous detail stems from the fact that extremely small – or local – disturbances have a major effect on the movements of the surrounding larger weather systems. The United States Weather Service has estimated that the 50 states experience as many as 10,000 different types of weather – each one of them potentially important to the life of a major weather development – at any given time.

A single cloud can change the entire course of a region's weather. For example, every storm starts life as a cumulus cloud, but it is largely a matter of chance which cloud becomes a hurricane. Satellite photographs have revealed that an individual cloud is usually part of an organized pattern of clouds. There is still much to learn about this organization before a particular kind of movement can be predicted for a certain cloud. Laser beams, (the word comes from Light Amplification by Stimulated Emission of Radiation) let scientists see the inside of a cloud and measure the different temperatures and air currents that each cloud contains. This research may soon remove some of the mystery surrounding the formation of hurricanes.

Satellites fitted with sensitive recording and measuring instruments already scan the globe, providing a wealth of raw data for computers to process and analyze. Several of these weather satellites are in fixed, or geosynchronous orbits, which means they observe a particular area of the globe all of the time. Although these constant observations provide accurate information, scientists would like to increase the accuracy by resolving some of the problems caused by the individual satellite's spin as it travels in its orbit.

Another promising area is the surface of the sea. As satellites fitted with radar equipment scan the surface of the oceans, meteorologists are beginning to get more data about winds at sea. Since the state of the sea is dependent on surface winds, the measurements may provide clues as to the nature of the surface/wind relationship.

As meteorological knowledge is increased by the use of sophisticated measuring devices and computer systems, a single fact emerges: the world's weather must be seen as a series of interrelated systems. What happens in the upper layers of the atmosphere cannot be understood without looking at the lower layers. What happens in the oceans must be studied in conjunction with what happens on land and in the air above both ground and water.

Although the prediction of tomorrow's weather becomes easier for meteorologists to state in accurate detail, the era of accurate long-range forecasting is still to come. Even when scientists understand some of the complex relationships between localized weather events and the bigger picture, they may never be able to say in June who will have sunshine on August 12 and who will get rain.

Accurate forecasting depends on understanding the relationship between general air movements and small-scale atmospheric disturbances of the sort these altocumulus clouds suggest.

Glossary

Anticyclone: an area of high pressure, often called simply a high, resulting from downward motion in the atmosphere. Weather in an anticyclone is usually dry

Atmosphere: the thin envelope of air that surrounds the earth, held to the surface by the pull of gravity

Atmospheric pressure: the weight of a column of air extending from a point (usually the ground) to the outer limit of the atmosphere

Barometer: an instrument that measures atmospheric pressure

Blizzard: heavy snow or blowing snow accompanied by winds 35 miles per hour or stronger

Climate: the combination of all the weather that a place experiences over a period of many months, years, or centuries

Cloud: very small liquid water droplets or ice crystals suspended in the atmosphere

Cold front: the dividing zone between two air masses of contrasting temperature, in which the cold air mass is displacing the warm air mass. After a cold front has passed, the weather gets colder

Condensation: the process in which water vapor turns into liquid water and releases latent heat to the surrounding atmosphere, as in the formation of cloud, fog or dew

Condensation level: the level at which rising air becomes saturated with water vapor

Convergence: an accumulation of air in a particular area caused by air moving into the area from different directions. When this happens the air is forced to rise

Coriolis effect: the apparent deflection of wind, to the right in the northern hemisphere and to the left in the southern, caused by the rotation of the earth

Corona: a small colored ring, reddish on the outside and bluish on the inside, seen around the sun or moon when cloud composed of water droplets is present

Depression: an area of low atmospheric pressure, often called simply a low, resulting from upward motion in the atmosphere. Weather in a depression is cloudy and wet, often with strong winds

Dew: a deposit of water that forms on the ground on clear nights when the air cools sufficiently to become saturated with water vapor

Drizzle: precipitation consisting of small droplets of water about 0.008 inch in diameter

Equinox: the dates (on or near March 21 and September 21) when day and night are of equal length all over the earth and the sun is overhead at midday on the Equator

Evaporation: the process by which liquid water turns into water vapor, gaining energy in the form of heat from the body of liquid water

Fog: tiny water droplets suspended in the air near the ground

Foehn: a warm, very dry wind blowing down a mountain slope

Frost: a thin deposit of ice which forms on the ground and other surfaces when water vapor condenses below 32°F

Hail: precipitation consisting of small pellets of hard ice

Halo: a large ring of whitish light seen around the sun or moon when clouds composed of ice crystals are present

Haze: fine dust particles dispersed through a layer of atmosphere, causing a reduction in visibility

Humidity: a measure of the amount of moisture in the air. Meteorologists usually measure relative humidity, which is the percentage of water vapor in the air compared with the total amount that would be needed to saturate the air

Hurricane: a very intense depression about 250 miles across that forms over most tropical oceans and brings extremely strong winds and torrential rain. A hurricane is called a typhoon by the Japanese and a cyclone by Australians

Isobar: a line on a weather map connecting places that have the same atmospheric pressure

Isopleth: a line on a weather map connecting places where a specific feature of the weather (for example, pressure or temperature) is constant

Jet stream: a belt of strong winds (70–180 miles per hour), usually in the upper atmosphere at heights of 3 to 6 miles

Lightning: the visible discharge of electricity associated with a thunderstorm

Occluded front: the combination of two fronts as a cold front overtakes a warm front

Polar front: the zone in temperate latitudes where cold air flowing from the polar regions meets warm air flowing from the subtropics

Precipitation: any form of water (for example, rain, drizzle, sleet, snow or hail) falling to the ground from a cloud

Radiosonde: a miniature radio transmitter with instruments for measuring atmospheric pressure, temperature and humidity, attached to a hydrogen- or helium-filled balloon

Rain: precipitation consisting of droplets of water larger than about 0.07 inch in diameter

Rainbow: a colored arc in the sky formed when white light from the sun is refracted and reflected by raindrops and split into its constituent colors

Rain shadow: the side of a mountain that is sheltered from a prevailing moist wind, where rainfall is less than in neighboring, more exposed areas.

Ridge: an elongated area of relatively high pressure

Saturated: air is saturated if it contains as much water vapor as it can hold at that temperature

Sea breeze: a wind that blows from the sea to the land caused only by the temperature difference between the sea and land surfaces

Sleet: precipitation consisting of ice particles, caused by the freezing of rain as it falls through a layer of cold air near the surface

Smog: fog mixed with pollutants such as smoke and exhaust gases

Snow: precipitation consisting of small ice crystals formed directly from water vapor and often sticking together to form snowflakes

Solstice: the dates (on or near June 21 and December 21) when the sun is overhead at midday on the northern or southern tropic. Days are longest and the sun highest in one hemisphere, shortest and lowest in the other

Stable: an air mass is stable if its temperature decreases only slowly, or even increases, with height. Stable air encourages the development of layer clouds

Stratosphere: the layer of the atmosphere, above about 6 miles, in which temperature either increases or stays the same as you go up

Synoptic chart: a map using isobars to show the position of depressions, anticyclones and fronts

Thunder: the noise that usually follows lightning, produced by a violent expansion of air

Tornado: a violent whirlwind which can lift heavy objects and cause great damage and loss of life, often accompanied by thunder, heavy rain or hail

Troposphere: the lowest layer of the atmosphere, extending from ground level up to between 5 and 10 miles

Trough: an area of relatively low pressure, often associated with a front, extending out from a depression

Unsaturated: air is unsaturated if it does not contain the maximum amount of moisture that it could hold at a particular temperature

Unstable: an air mass is unstable if its temperature decreases rapidly with height. Unstable air encourages the development of tall clouds and showers

Warm front: the dividing zone between two air masses of contrasting temperature in which the warm air is displacing the cold air. After a warm front has passed, the weather gets warmer and often humid

Wind: a moving mass of air. The direction of a wind is the direction from which the air is coming

Weather: the state of the earth's atmosphere at a particular place and time, especially the state of temperature, humidity, cloudiness, wind and precipitation

Index

Credits

The Publishers gratefully acknowledge permission to reproduce the following illustrations:

ANP Foto, Amsterdam 50; Ardea London 77*tl*; from: Bruce W. Atkinson 'The Weather Business', Aldus Books 68; Barnaby's Picture Library 37, 45*tl, tc, c,* 47; BBC Hulton Picture Library 85; Biofotos 41*br*; British Airports Authority 74*l*; British Antarctic Survey 86; Camera Press Ltd. 53, 83*r*; G. P. Carruthers 66*b*; J. Allan Cash Ltd. 46; Bruce Coleman Ltd. 31, 34, 35, 75*b*, 77*b*, 80*r*; Cornish Photo News 74*r*; Crown Copyright/reproduced with the permission of the Controller, Her Majesty's Stationery Office 63*b*, 65*b*, 69, 71, 72, 73*b*; Daily Telegraph Colour Library 15*l*, 15*r* (Masterfile); Dundee University 17; Elisabeth Photo Library, London Ltd. 81*l*; Fortean Picture Library 43*r*; Susan Griggs Agency Ltd. 52; Robert Harding Picture Library 49, 60, 61*b*, 80*l*, 87*t*; Alan Hutchison Library 29, 45*r*; Institute of Geological Sciences (NERC Copyright) 87*b*; Frank W. Lane 41*bl*, 51, 55*r*, 57; Lockyer Collection 43*l*; Edward Marcus Ltd., London 62; R. W. Mason 41*tr*; NASA 54, 67; Alec Nisbett 88, 89; Novosti Press Agency 32*r*; W. G. Pendleton 41*cl*; Photri 21; Pictor International Ltd. 75*t*, 84; Popperfoto 32*l*, 48, 78, 83*l*; H. O. F. Robbins 59*t*; Royal Meteorological Society 45*bl*; Royal Signals and Radar Establishment, Malvern: Crown Copyright Reserved 73*t*; Science Photo Library 25 (Courtesy of ITEK Corporation), 65*t* (National Center for Atmospheric Research); John Sims 19, 41*t*, 91; Space Frontiers Ltd. 66*t*; Stockphotos International 27, 40, 93; John Topham Picture Library 55*l*; Trewin Copplestone Books Ltd. 79*r*, 81*r*; U.S. Department of Energy 61*t*; Vision International/ Paulo Koch 79*l*; Peter Wright 41*bc*, 58; W. K. Young 59*b*; ZEFA 3, 9, 10, 39, 41*cc*, 63*t*, 77*tr*.

Cover Photograph: Stockphotos International

Artwork by: Brown Wells & Jacobs Ltd. 13; Kai Choi 18; Tom McArthur 11, 12, 24, 27, 38, 42, 56, 57, 58; Carol McCleeve 15, 20*b*, 22, 25, 30*t*, 64; Sid Roderick 8.

Bibliography

Atmosphere, Weather, and Climate (3rd edn.), R. G. Barry and R. J. Chorley (eds.); Methuen 1978.
Clouds, Rain, and Rainmaking, B. J. Mason; Cambridge University Press 1975.
Guiness Book of Weather Facts and Feats, Ingrid Holford (ed.); Guiness 1977.
Introduction to Meteorology (3rd edn.), Franklin W. Cole; John Wiley 1980.
The Observer's Book of Weather, Robert Pearce; Frederick Warne 1980.
Understanding Climatic Change (1st edn.), U.S. Committee for the Global Atmospheric Research Program; National Academy of Science 1975.